Teenage Health

Series Editor: Cara Acred

Volume 324

Independence Educational Publishers

First published by Independence Educational Publishers

The Studio, High Green

Great Shelford

Cambridge CB22 5EG

England

© Independence 2017

Copyright

Photocopy licence

ISBN-13: 978 1 86168 774 6

Printed in Great Britain

Zenith Print Group

Contents

Chapter 1: Physical health

Key statistics about children and young people 1

Teenagers 'crying out' for early help with mental health problems 4

Mental health – how are children and young people affected? 5

Stigma stopping young people talking about mental health 6

Suicide by children and young people in England 7

Exam stress linked to teen suicide 10

New study warns of confidence crisis amongst British teenagers 11

Young people's health – the latest trends 13

Report highlights loneliness and lack of social integration amongst young people 14

Chapter 2: Lifestyle choices

New ESPAD results: teenage drinking and smoking down, but concerns posed by new drugs and new addictive behaviours 15

Young people and smoking 16

Iceland knows how to stop teen substance abuse but the rest of the world isn't listening 19

What we know about young people in alcohol and drug treatment 24

More than a quarter of young adults in the UK do not drink alcohol – in data 25

Use of electronic cigarettes among children in Great Britain 26

Social media is nothing like drugs, despite all the horror stories 28

Children "becoming hunchbacks" due to addiction to smartphones 30

Chapter 3: Physical health

Physical activity levels tail off in boys and girls from age seven 31

Adolescents: health risks and solutions 32

Why sugar is so much worse for teenagers' brains 34

Why is diabetes killing so many teenagers? 35

One in three older teenagers have been too stressed to sleep 36

Protecting teenagers in the UK against meningitis 37

Are you ready for sex? 38

Key facts 40

Glossary 41

Assignments 42

Index 43

Acknowledgements 44

Introduction

TEENAGE HEALTH is Volume 324 in the **ISSUES** series. The aim of the series is to offer current, diverse information about important issues in our world, from a UK perspective.

ABOUT TITLE

Teenage health encompasses a wide range of ailments, both physical and emotional. This book explores mental health issues such as depression and anxiety – both of which can be influenced by exam stress, among other things – alongside 'risky behaviours' such as smoking and drinking. It also looks at illnesses such as diabetes and meningitis, as well as sexual health.

OUR SOURCES

Titles in the **ISSUES** series are designed to function as educational resource books, providing a balanced overview of a specific subject.

The information in our books is comprised of facts, articles and opinions from many different sources, including:

⇨ Newspaper reports and opinion pieces

⇨ Website factsheets

⇨ Magazine and journal articles

⇨ Statistics and surveys

⇨ Government reports

⇨ Literature from special interest groups.

A NOTE ON CRITICAL EVALUATION

Because the information reprinted here is from a number of different sources, readers should bear in mind the origin of the text and whether the source is likely to have a particular bias when presenting information (or when conducting their research). It is hoped that, as you read about the many aspects of the issues explored in this book, you will critically evaluate the information presented.

It is important that you decide whether you are being presented with facts or opinions. Does the writer give a biased or unbiased report? If an opinion is being expressed, do you agree with the writer? Is there potential bias to the 'facts' or statistics behind an article?

ASSIGNMENTS

In the back of this book, you will find a selection of assignments designed to help you engage with the articles you have been reading and to explore your own opinions. Some tasks will take longer than others and there is a mixture of design, writing and research-based activities that you can complete alone or in a group.

Useful weblinks

www.ash.org.uk

www.blog.ons.gov.uk

www.childrenssociety.org.uk

www.theconversation.com

www.corporate.sky.com

www.counselling-directory.org

www.espad.org

www.theguardian.com

www.independent.co.uk

www.kcl.ac.uk

www.natcen.ac.uk

www.nhs.uk

www.princes-trust.org.uk

www.publichealthmatters.blog.gov.uk

www.research.bmh.manchester.ac.uk

www.telegraph.co.uk

www.who.int

FURTHER RESEARCH

At the end of each article we have listed its source and a website that you can visit if you would like to conduct your own research. Please remember to critically evaluate any sources that you consult and consider whether the information you are viewing is accurate and unbiased.

Key statistics about children and young people

According to the Mental Health Foundation, nearly one in ten children and young people aged five to 16 are affected by a mental health problem.

Despite the knowledge and awareness of mental health being on the rise, alarmingly, 70% of young people who experience a mental health problem do not receive the appropriate support.[1] The emotional well-being of children and young people is just as important as their physical health. The early years of adulthood are a crucial time as the mind and body are rapidly developing and children are constantly facing new challenges.

One in ten children and young people are affected by a mental health problem

In this article, we will explore teenage mental health and the common areas of mental distress for children and young people.

Children are extremely vulnerable to mental disorders. Unlike adults, who have the ability to identify, understand and seek help for a problem, a child may be confused and upset by what they are feeling. Fortunately, there are now many organisations working to spread awareness and end the stigma of mental distress. These organisations are a place for young people to receive the support they need to progress into young adults.

While many children will grow up mentally healthy, the Mental Health Foundation report that the number of those experiencing problems has risen compared to 30 years ago. Many factors will contribute to how the mind develops and how well a child will be able to cope with the changes happening to their body.

Some of the most common mental health problems affecting children and young people include:

⇨ depression

⇨ self-harm

⇨ generalised anxiety disorder (GAD)

⇨ post-traumatic stress disorder (PTSD)

⇨ attention deficit hyperactivity disorder (ADHD)

⇨ eating disorders.[2]

In the 2014/15 Child Line review, the results for the top ten reasons why young people contact Child Line show their main areas of concern. The top concern for young people was family relationships, including conflict in the family and parents' divorce or separation. Over 12 months, there were over 38,000 counselling sessions for this concern.

Following family relationships, other concerns for children and young people included:

Risk factors

There are some risk factors that can make some children more likely to experience problems than others. While most things that happen in a young person's life will not

Main concerns	Number of counselling sessions
Low self-esteem, feeling sad, low or lonely.	35,244
Abuse, including sexual, online, physical, emotional and neglect.	29,126
Bullying, face-to-face or online.	25,736
Self-harm	19,557

lead to mental health problems, certain traumatic events can trigger problems for children who are already considered vulnerable. Some of the risk factors include:

⇨ Having a long-term physical illness.

⇨ Having a parent who has problems with alcohol or drugs.

⇨ Having a parent who has had mental health problems.

⇨ Experiencing the death of a loved one.

⇨ Having parents who are separated.

⇨ Being severely bullied or abused.

⇨ Living in poverty.

⇨ Experiencing discrimination.

⇨ Living in care.

⇨ Taking on adult responsibilities at a young age.

The Young Minds charity reported that, in 2008, 72% of children living in care were experiencing behavioural or emotional problems. These children were regarded as some of the most vulnerable people in UK society.

Common areas of mental distress

Anxiety and anxiety-related problems

Anxiety problems are incredibly common. It is thought that as many as one in six young people will experience an anxiety-related problem.[3] Children and young people suffering from anxiety may experience it in three forms:

⇨ Affecting one in 25 people in the UK, generalised anxiety disorder (GAD) can cause young people to feel extremely worried. Young children starting a new school may suffer separation anxiety.[4]

⇨ Panic attacks are unpredictable attacks of extreme anxiety, usually lasting around ten minutes. The sufferer may find it difficult to breathe and feel out of control. The feelings of panic will gradually start to ease but the person can be left quite shaken and uneasy.

⇨ Those who live with a phobia tend to feel nervous about one thing in particular. While to some people it may not be dangerous or threatening, to the person with the phobia, it can be quite detrimental to everyday life. For example, agoraphobia, the fear of being in situations where escape may be difficult.

Attention deficit hyperactivity disorder (ADHD)

Children with ADHD may find it difficult to concentrate, have a lot of energy and say things without thinking. ADHD in children is thought to start at around 18 months old, however, symptoms often only become apparent between ages three and seven. ADHD is more common in boys than in girls, affecting one to two children in every 100. It is the most common behavioural disorder in children.[5]

Eating disorders

According to The Royal College of Psychiatrists, the two most common eating problems are anorexia nervosa and bulimia nervosa. Eating disorders commonly start during the teenage years, though they can occur at any time. It is believed that eating problems are seven to ten times more common in girls than boys.

Binge-eating disorder (sometimes described as compulsive eating), is when an individual feels they cannot stop themselves from eating, even if they want to. It is common for the sufferer to rely on food for emotional support or to mask difficult feelings.

There is no single cause to an eating disorder, but it is estimated that almost 1.6 million people in the UK are affected.[6]

Depression

Depression is a common mental disorder that affects nearly 80,000 children and young people. Many people think depression is only prevalent in adults, but in fact 2% of children under 12 years old will experience depression.[7]

Most young people will occasionally feel upset or low, but some can feel sad, lonely, anxious or stressed for longer periods of time. It is when people feel this way for a long time that it starts to affect their daily life.

Self-harm

It can be difficult to understand why people self-harm, but it is more common than people think. The Mental Health Foundation reported that between one in 12 and one in 15 people self-harm. Some research suggests that the UK has the highest rate of self-harm in Europe.

However, many young people who self-harm will not harm themselves in a way that requires medical attention, so the numbers only show part of the picture. The stigma of teenage mental health needs to be removed so that young people can get the help they need.

Suicidal feelings

While everyone has times when they feel down and can't see a way out, young people can be particularly vulnerable to suicidal feelings. Thoughts of the future, school pressures, relationships and sexuality can sometimes become overwhelming.

Young people feeling this way may believe that nobody can help them or that they have no one to talk to. It is

Mental health statistics: children and young people

One in ten affected by mental health problem

72% of children in care experience emotional problems

One in six young people will experience anxiety related problems

2% of children under 12 will experience depression

Source: Counselling Directory

these feelings that can lead a person to believe that the only way out is to end their life.

According to a 2011 report by the Office for National Statistics (ONS), almost 200 15- to 19-year-olds and over 400 20- to 24-year-olds committed suicide. Despite this alarming figure, not all of those experiencing suicidal feelings go on to take their life. It is important to let young people know that support is available and they are not alone.

Child abuse

Child abuse is any action that causes significant harm to a child. It can be physical, emotional or sexual but can also be a lack of love, care and attention. Neglect can be just as damaging to a child as physical abuse. The NSPCC estimate that more than half a million children in the UK are abused each year.

They report that in 2014–2015, there were over 29,000 counselling sessions with young people contacting Child Line about abuse. The main concerns of these calls were sexual and physical abuse.

It is positive to see more young people finding the courage to contact support services. In 2014, the charity reported seeing an 8% rise in

young people calling about sexual abuse. Despite this, 15% of callers said the abuse had been happening for a long time and 30% said the abuse happened in the past.

Many young people described feelings of shame and confusion and often believed they were to blame. In 33% of counselling sessions, young people would explain how they had never told anybody about the abuse. But when reassured that they were not responsible, many felt a "huge sense of relief".

How can counselling help?

The stigma and judgements associated with teenage mental health can make it tough for children and young people to find the courage to seek help. While they may not be in the position to talk to a friend, family member or teacher, it is important to spread awareness of the help available.

Children and young people may benefit from professional support. There are various treatments that can help young people understand and cope with what they are going through, including talking and creative therapies.

Counselling provides the young person with the opportunity to

explore their feelings. Here they can open up about their problems without shame or discrimination. The counsellor is someone to listen and offer support to the child, who may otherwise feel alone.

Common forms of therapy often recommended include:

⇨ cognitive behavioural therapy (CBT)

⇨ cognitive analytical therapy (CAT)

⇨ arts therapies

⇨ counselling and psychotherapy

⇨ mindfulness

⇨ play therapy.

References

1 Mental Health Foundation: Children and Young People. https://www.mentalhealth.org.uk/a-to-z/c/children-and-young-people

2 Young Minds: Mental Health Statistics. http://www.youngminds.org.uk/training_services/policy/mental_health_statistics

3, 4 Young Minds: Anxiety. http://www.youngminds.org.uk/for_children_young_people/whats_worrying_you/anxiety/what_is_anxiety

5 Young Minds: ADHD. http://www.youngminds.org.uk/for_children_young_people/whats_worrying_you/adhd/what_is_adhd

6 Mind: Types of Eating Disorders. http://www.mind.org.uk/information-support/types-of-mental-health-problems/eating-problems/types-of-eating-disorders/?o=6260#bingeeatingdisorder

7 Young Minds: Depression. http://www.youngminds.org.uk/for_children_young_people/whats_worrying_you/depression/what_is_depression Page last reviewed: 19/02/16

14 July 2017

⇨ The above information is reprinted with kind permission from the Counselling Directory. Please visit www.counselling-directory.org/young-people-stats.html for further information.

Teenagers 'crying out' for early help with mental health problems

School children should be supported to spot the early signs of mental and emotional stress so they can get help soon enough to prevent problems escalating into long-term mental illness, according to The Children's Society.

The charity, which campaigns and provides services for children in poverty and teenagers at risk of neglect, is calling for investment in prevention and early intervention services – including in schools – to address problems before they can develop into more serious conditions.

As part of this it is calling for a national focus on positive mental health, emotional well-being and resilience in schools and communities, through the curriculum as well as through targeted support.

The pre-election announcement of £1.25 billion funding for children and adolescent mental health services in this year's budget statement was welcome. But The Children's Society argues it is vital that this funding is fully ring-fenced to make sure local areas can invest it in early intervention and specialist services, including targeted support for vulnerable older teenagers and victims of child sexual exploitation.

In recent years, support services have been significantly undermined by insecure or short-term funding, or have been shut down altogether. Investment in Children and Adolescents' Mental Health Services (CAMHS) has reached a tipping point with real-terms cuts of £79 million over a three-year period despite the growing number of young people requiring mental health support.

The charity is calling for better access and support for the most vulnerable groups of young people who can often by overlooked by services, including older teenagers and those who may have experienced, or are at risk of, sexual abuse, domestic violence or homelessness.

It is also concerned that an increase in child poverty could lead to an increase in demand for child and adolescent mental health services. It plans to investigate how child mental health is impacted by debt, poor housing, unemployment, isolation and poor access to services.

The Children's Society, which already offers a range of counselling, befriending and emotional support services, including in schools, is planning to expand its mental health work following evidence from its frontline services that mental health problems among vulnerable young people are significant and growing. It has published a policy paper setting out the organisation's priorities for improving children's mental health services in the coming years.

The organisation's focus on mental health and emotional well-being comes against a backdrop of pressures on young people, such as exams, constant access to social media, and with research showing that many teenagers' self-esteem and emotional well-being are worryingly low.

Matthew Reed, Chief Executive of The Children's Society, said: "Children and young people are under huge pressures and yet they are made to wait to receive the help they need with issues like depression or anxiety, if they are able to access help at all.

"The mental health needs of the most vulnerable young people in particular are so often overlooked when they are crying out for help to deal with the emotional impact of abuse and neglect.

"We believe schools are the ideal places to start identifying and meeting the mental health and emotional needs of pupils at an early stage. They offer a safe environment for children and young people to address issues that can have an impact on mental health, such as low self-esteem, bullying, and exam anxiety.

"Through our work, we know all these issues can be early warning signs of future risks for young people such as running away, falling into gangs, and even being at risk of exploitation and abuse.

"That's why we are asking Government to ring-fence investment in this area, and why we hope to use our experience and expertise to prevent children's mental health problems having lasting effects.'

Notes to editors:

• The Children's Society's policy paper, *Children's Mental Health: Priorities for Improving Children and Adolescent Mental Health Services in England*, is available.

• The last official research into the prevalence of mental ill health among children took place in 2004, when a survey by the Office for National Statistics found that one in ten children up to the age of 16 suffer from mental health issues. That is the equivalent of about three children in every classroom.

• The Children's Society has studied children's subjective well-being since 2005. Our Good Childhood Inquiry, launched in 2006, was the first independent national inquiry into childhood that sought to better understand modern childhood from children themselves. We have since produced regular reports reviewing children's subjective well-being and have analysed the impact of a range of aspects affecting the way children feel about their lives.

• The Children's Society has helped change children's stories for over a century. We expose injustice and address hard truths, tackling child poverty and neglect head-on. We fight for change based on the experiences of every child we work with and the solid evidence we gather. Through our campaigning, commitment and care, we are determined to give every child in this country the greatest possible chance in life. For more information visit: childrenssociety.org.uk.

17 June 2015

⇨ The above information is reprinted with kind permission from The Children's Society. Please visit www.childrenssociety.org.uk for further information.

Mental health – how are children and young people affected?

In February we marked Children's Mental Health Week – a week dedicated to equipping children with the tools to maintain good mental health. Mental health and the provision of services to support children and young people with mental health disorders are at the forefront of public health policy, having been "dangerously disregarded as secondary to physical health", according to the Prime Minister. The Health Secretary Jeremy Hunt has also pledged to improve children's mental health services. Initiatives like Children's Mental Health Week are great ways of raising awareness to continue this improvement.

So what do we know about children's mental health, and the provision of these services, at the moment?

The most recent comprehensive survey data we have on young people's mental health is from 2004 when it was found that around one in ten young people aged between five and 16 had a clinically diagnosed mental disorder.

Boys were more likely than girls to have a mental disorder (11% compared with 8%). Also, older children were more likely to have a mental disorder (12% of 11–16-year-olds compared to eight per cent of five to ten-year-olds).

Throughout the last 13 years, there has been some research into certain elements of children and young people's mental health and service provision, which gives us some idea of the state of things at the moment.

ONS research into children's mental health and well-being found that one in eight children aged ten to 15 reported symptoms of mental ill-health in 2011 to 2012. Looking at data from a Strengths and Difficulties questionnaire, which screens the behaviour of children aged two to 17, it also found children who spent over three hours on social websites on a normal school night were more than twice as likely to show symptoms of mental ill-health.

One report by the Education Policy Institute in April 2016 found that on average, specialist child and adolescent mental health services are turning away almost a quarter of the young people referred to them for help. Children had to wait one month on average for a first appointment, and two months until the start of treatment.

What's next?

The world has changed a lot since the last comprehensive young people's mental health survey. In 2004, Facebook had just launched, the iPhone was still three years from its launch and the first tweet was yet to be sent on Twitter. We therefore need new national survey data that can provide updated estimates on the prevalence of mental health disorders in children and young people across England, particularly in this age of social media. This evidence will help to shape government policy and decisions in this area and make sure services are meeting the needs of today's children and young people.

NatCen and the Office of National Statistics (ONS), on behalf of NHS Digital, have recently launched the National Study of Health and Wellbeing – a study which has this as its primary aim. The survey will cover 9,500 children and young people aged two–19 years old, and provide estimates on the prevalence of mental health disorders of children and young people in England. The study incorporates standardised tools that measure psychological well-being and mental health, such as the Strengths and Difficulties Questionnaire (SDQ) and Development and Wellbeing Assessment (DAWBA) – developed by YouthInMind who is our collaborator on this study. The survey will also provide data on various topics such as cyberbullying, social media and service use.

Interviews are well under way and will be in field until late summer 2017. We expect that the findings will be published in 2018. The results will provide more information about the mental health of children and young people, helping the Government, NHS and wider society to better understand and support those facing mental health issues.

15 May 2017

⇨ The above information is reprinted with kind permission from NatCen Social Research and ONS. Please visit www.blog.ons.gov.uk for further information.

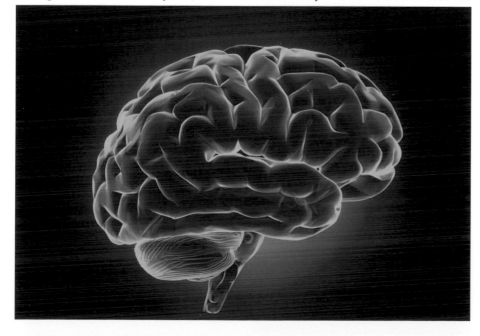

Stigma stopping young people talking about mental health

Our new research reveals that one in four young people (24%) would not confide in someone if they were experiencing a mental health problem, with many fearing that it could affect their job prospects.

The research, funded by Macquarie, based on a survey of 2,215 respondents aged 16 to 25, found that the vast majority of young people (78%) think there is a stigma attached to mental health issues.

A third (32%) of those young people who would keep quiet about their mental health worries think admitting to a problem could affect their job prospects, 57% wouldn't want anyone to know they were struggling and 35% fear it would make them "look weak".

Conducted anonymously online, the research found that almost half (47%) of young people have experienced a mental health issue. These young people are:

⇨ Significantly less likely to feel in control of their job prospects[i]

⇨ More likely to feel too tired and stressed to cope with day-to-day life[ii]

⇨ More likely to feel they have less control over their education, training or finances[iii] than their peers.

The findings were published today in part two of The Prince's Trust *Macquarie Youth Index*.

Part one was published in January this year and found that the overall wellbeing of young people in the UK is at its lowest point on the Index since the study was first commissioned in 2009[iv] – with one in four young people not feeling in control of their lives.

In the last year alone, the number of young people supported by The Prince's Trust who are experiencing mental health problems has increased by 16%.[vi] In light of these findings, and in a bid to inspire and empower young people, we're calling for people to post on Twitter using the hashtag #TakeControl about the things they do, big or small, that help them to feel in control of their lives.[v]

Dame Martina Milburn DCVO CBE, our Chief Executive, said:

"We know issues like depression and anxiety can have a crippling impact on a young person's aspirations and life chances, so it's alarming to find that so many would rather live with mental health issues than talk to anyone about them.

"We must all work together to instil confidence in these young people that they won't be stigmatised, and one of the key things we can do to help improve their mental health is to help them with their education, training and job prospects.

"Our personal development programmes give young people the self-esteem and coping skills that set them up not just for the workplace but for life."

David Fass, CEO of Macquarie Group, EMEA said:

"It is concerning that one of the reasons young people are reluctant to talk openly about their mental health is that they think it will negatively affect their job prospects. At Macquarie, we encourage our people to bring their whole selves to work and understand that sometimes everyone needs a bit of extra support. Organisations like The Prince's Trust can help young people to develop the skills and confidence they need to build the future they want; and that's why, as UK employers, we are proud to support this important research."

Professor Louise Arseneault, ESRC Mental Health Leadership Fellow at the Institute of Psychiatry, Psychology & Neuroscience (IoPPN), King's College London said:

"It is extremely worrying to see that young people suffer from the stigma around mental health. This can be a major obstacle for them in seeking help and finding support, which could further affect their confidence in finding work at a crucial stage in their lives. It shouldn't be like this.

"Increasing the understanding and awareness of mental health problems among young people should be a key priority. We also need to explore ways of ensuring young people with mental health problems do not fall out of education or employment from an early age."

As part of our ongoing commitment to help young people overcome any emotional well-being challenges that may be holding them back in life, we've launched a new mental health strategy to give our staff, volunteers and delivery partners the confidence and ability to respond to young people's mental health needs.

We have appointed Chris Harris as our first Mental Health Advisor, a new post funded by Royal Mail Group, and we are forming new partnerships with mental health organisations and specialist services, with the aim of co-locating mental health services at Prince's Trust Centres.

Mental health support will be embedded in all our employability and personal development programmes to help vulnerable young people access the most appropriate care at the earliest opportunity.

[i] 42% of respondents who have experienced a mental health problem don't feel in control of their job prospects, compared to 31% of respondents who have not experienced a mental health problem.

[ii] 47% of respondents who have experienced a mental health problem feel too tired and stressed to cope with day to day life, compared to 21% of respondents who have not experienced a mental health problem.

[iii] 24% of respondents who have experienced a mental health problem don't feel in control of their education or training, compared to 12% of respondents who have not experienced a mental health problem. 44% of respondents who have experienced a mental health problem don't feel in control of their finances, compared to 25% of respondents who have not experienced a mental health problem.

[iv] The index, which measures levels of happiness and confidence, has decreased by one point – down from 71 to 70 in the last 12 months.

[v] Posts must be on Facebook, Twitter or Instagram and include the hashtag #TakeControl so that young people can easily find relevant posts.

[vi] Financial year 2014–2015. A fifth (21%) of the young people who are supported by The Trust consider themselves to have a mental health problem.

1 March 2017

⇨ The above information is reprinted with kind permission from The Prince's Trust. Please visit www. princes-trust.org.uk for further information.

Suicide by children and young people in England

An extract from a report from The University of Manchester.

How we carried out the study

We carried out an examination of suicides in England by people aged under 20 years who died between January 2014 and April 2015. This is the first phase of a UK-wide investigation into suicides by people aged under 25.

We collected data from a range of investigations by official bodies in England. The study did not conduct new investigations. We identified relevant antecedents prior to suicide from these investigations.

Main findings

There were 145 suicides and probable suicides by children and young people in England in the study period. The suicide rate in this age group is low overall but is highest in the late teens. The majority of deaths were in males (70%).

Over a quarter (28%) had been bereaved – 13% by the suicide of a family member or friend. Over a third (36%) had a physical health condition, the most common conditions being acne and asthma. Academic pressures were common antecedents, almost a third (29%) of those in education were facing exams or exam results at the time of death.

Bullying, mostly historical, was reported in 22%. Online bullying was less common than face-to-face bullying. Social isolation or withdrawal were reported in 25%. Suicide-related Internet use was an antecedent in 23% of deaths.

The majority (54%) had indicated their risk through previous self-harm, and around a quarter (27%) had expressed suicidal ideas in the week before they died. Almost half (43%) were not known to any service or agency.

Most antecedents of suicide – exam pressures, abuse, bullying, bereavement, physical health conditions and self-harm – were more common in the females who died.

Abuse, academic pressures and bullying were more common in under-18s, while excessive drinking, illicit drug use and serious self-harm were more common in 18–19-year-olds.

Key messages

Suicide rates rise sharply in the late teens; numerous factors appear to contribute to this.

Many young people who die by suicide have not expressed recent suicidal ideas. An absence of suicidal ideas cannot be assumed to show lack of risk.

Agencies that work with young people can contribute to suicide prevention by recognising the pattern of cumulative risk and "final straw" stresses that leads to suicide. Improved services for self-harm and access to CAMHS are crucial to addressing suicide and there is a vital role for schools, primary care, social services and youth justice.

Ten common themes in suicide by children and young people:

⇨ family factors such as mental illness

⇨ abuse and neglect

⇨ bereavement and experience of suicide

⇨ bullying

⇨ suicide-related Internet use

⇨ academic pressures, especially related to exams

⇨ social isolation or withdrawal

⇨ physical health conditions that may have social impact

⇨ alcohol and illicit drugs

⇨ mental ill health, self-harm and suicidal ideas

Report coverage

This report covers phase one of a national investigation into suicide in children and young people. The study is being undertaken in two phases:

1. The first year has focused on people aged ten to 19 years who died by suicide (includes open verdicts) in England.

2. Data collection is now being extended to include people aged up to 24, in all UK countries. A further report will be published in 2017 and will include recommendations for services.

This report describes the antecedents of suicide by people aged under 20, based on deaths that occurred during a 16-month period.

Definitions

Suicides were deaths that received a conclusion of suicide or open verdict at coroner's inquest, as is conventional in research and national statistics.[1]

In line with the Office for National Statistics (ONS) procedures for identifying deaths by suicide, deaths coded with the following International Classification of Diseases, Tenth Revision (ICD–10)[2] codes were included in the study: X60–X84; Y10–Y34 (excluding Y33.9); Y87. Deaths receiving a narrative verdict at coroner inquest were included in the study if ONS procedures for identifying suicide deaths applied one of these ICD–10 codes.

Notification of deaths by suicide of children and young people

National suicide data were obtained from ONS for individuals aged between ten and 19 during the first year of the study. These deaths occurred between January 2014 and April 2015. In total, 145 deaths by suicide were notified by ONS in the time period (table on page nine).

Data were received from one or more of the following data sources for 130 (90%) individuals.

1. Coroner inquest hearings (127 cases)

Audio CDs of inquest hearings were requested in all cases. Coroners were sent the name(s) of individuals who died by suicide in their jurisdiction and asked to provide a CD recording of the inquest hearing (or where not available, copy statements or depositions submitted as evidence).

2. Child Death Overview Panel (CDOP) child death investigations (under 18 years only) (35 cases)

Local Safeguarding Children's Boards (LSCB) were asked to provide copies of any CDOP analysis proformas (Form C) in cases where the CDOP had reviewed the death of an individual by suicide or deliberate self-inflicted harm. Around a third of LSCBs did not participate, usually due to uncertainties over the release of personal data.

There were also LSCBs who had not reviewed, finalised or provided the Form C to the study at the time of writing.

3. Serious Case Reviews (5 cases)

Serious Case Reviews were sought from the National Society for the Prevention of Cruelty to Children (NSPCC) national case review repository[3] or from the relevant LSCB.

4. Criminal justice system reports (1 case)

The Prisons and Probation Ombudsman (PPO) agreed to notify the study when a new report meeting the study criteria was published and available to download on their website[4].

In addition, the Independent Police Complaints Commission (IPCC) agreed to notify the study when an investigation on an apparent suicide of a young person in or after release from custody was conducted.

5. National Confidential Inquiry into Suicide and Homicide by People with Mental Illness (NCISH) data (17 cases)

A full description of our own data collection processes can be found elsewhere. In brief:

⇨ patients (i.e. individuals in contact with mental health services within 12 months of suicide) were identified from mental health trust records

⇨ a detailed questionnaire was sent to the consultant psychiatrist responsible for the care of the patient.

17 (12%) individuals were identified as patients from our data. This is likely to increase as data collection is completed. The number of mental health patients is therefore an under-estimate at this stage.

6. NHS Serious Incident Review reports (18 cases)

For those individuals who were identified as patients from the NCISH database, the medical director at the NHS Trust where the patient was treated was asked to provide a copy of the NHS Serious Incident Review report.

Analysis

Information was taken from the sources listed above via a data extraction proforma on to a standardised database for aggregate analysis.

Descriptive data are presented as numbers and percentages. The denominator in all estimates was the total number of cases on which information was received (i.e. 130) unless otherwise specified. If an item was not recorded in any data source then it was assumed to be absent or not relevant.

Pearson's chi-square tests were used to examine associations between males and females, and between under-18s and 18–19-year-olds. Significant differences ($p < 0.05$) are highlighted in the table.

---

1. Linsley KR, Schapira K, Kelly TP. Open verdict v. suicide – importance to research. *British Journal of Psychiatry* 2001; 178:465-48.

2. World Health Organization (WHO). *International classification of diseases and related health problems 10th revision* (ICD–10). Geneva: World Health Organization, 2010.

3. NSPCC Library online. http://library.nspcc.org.uk/HeritageScripts/Hapi.dll/search2?&LabelText=Casereview&searchterm=*&Fields=@Media=SCR&Bool=AND

4. Prisons and Probation Ombudsman Independent Investigations. Fatal Incident reports. www.ppo.gov.uk/document/fiireport/

	Number (%)
Total deaths by suicide in children and young people (notified by ONS)	145
Deaths on which at least one report has been obtained	130 (90%)
Coroner inquest hearings received	127 (88%)
CDOP child death investigations received (under-18s only)	35 (53%) of deaths in under-18s
Single source of data received	80 (55%)

With this sample size, several differences were of borderline statistical significance.

What we found

Deaths notified in the study period

Numbers

We were notified by ONS of 145 deaths by suicide in people aged under 20 in the 16-month study period.

Age and gender

The number of suicides increased into the late teens.

The number of male suicides was higher than females, more obviously in the late teens, with a male to female ratio of 2.4:1 overall.

Method of suicide (figure below)

The most common method of suicide for males and females was hanging/strangulation. This was followed by jumping/multiple injuries, i.e. mainly being struck by a train (16, 11%) or jumping from a height (11, 8%). Females died by self-poisoning significantly more often than males, and males by jumping/multiple injuries. 65 (64%) males died by hanging, similar to the proportion of females (27, 63%). There were six deaths following gas inhalation.

Antecedents of suicide

We recorded information on 130 (90%) of the 145 children and young people who died by suicide in the study period. The remainder of the findings is based on these 130 individuals. 92 (71%) were male. 14 (11%) were from a black or minority ethnic group.

May 2016

⇨ Reproduced from: Suicide by children and young people in England. National Confidential Inquiry into Suicide and Homicide by People with Mental Illness (NCISH) Manchester 2016.

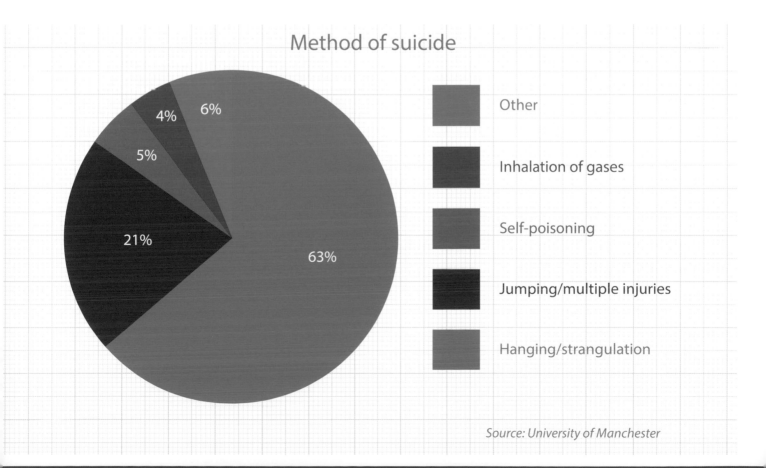

Method of suicide

- Other 6%
- Inhalation of gases 4%
- Self-poisoning 5%
- Jumping/multiple injuries 21%
- Hanging/strangulation 63%

Source: University of Manchester

Exam stress linked to teen suicide

"First detailed study into 130 [teen] suicide cases in England finds range of common anxieties," *The Guardian* reports, citing factors including exam stress, bullying and bereavement.

The study into teenage suicide also found there was a history of self-harming in half of suicide cases in young people.

Researchers identified multiple factors that might have contributed to the deaths.

These include having experienced bereavement, relationship problems or breakdown; having long-term physical health problems, including asthma and acne, family problems, self-harm, bullying, and alcohol or drug use.

It's unclear if any single factor was a cause of death. It could be possible that in many cases multiple risk factors triggered suicidal thinking and behaviour.

However, we cannot be sure that these factors contributed to the deaths of the children and young people involved in all cases. This is partly because they are very common.

For example, the study showed that 27% of those who died had experienced exam stress or other academic pressures, but we don't know what proportion of under-20s in the general population also experience exam stress.

One striking fact is that in 54% of cases there was a previous history of self-harm. And one in four had talked about suicide in the week before they died.

It's important to get help quickly if you are thinking about self-harming and suicide, or think a friend or relative may be affected by similar thinking and behaviour. Seek advice from your GP.

Where did the story come from?

The study was carried out by researchers from the National Confidential Inquiry into Suicide and Homicide by People with Mental Illness, based at the University of Manchester, and was funded by the Healthcare Quality Improvement Partnership.

It was published in the peer-reviewed journal *The Lancet Psychiatry* on an open-access basis, so it's free to read online.

Coverage in the UK media was widespread. Different organisations chose to highlight different factors from the report, perhaps reflecting their own interests.

For example, *The Sun* reported that, "The Internet played a role in a quarter of recent teen suicides in England", while the *Daily Mail* stated that, "Drugs linked to one in three teen suicides". *The Times*, *The Guardian* and *The Daily Telegraph* highlighted exam stress.

Not all news stories were clear that these factors cannot be seen as direct causes of suicide.

For example, most teenagers have exam stress and develop acne, and many dabble in drugs and alcohol. But, thankfully, most teenagers don't kill themselves.

The Guardian did the best job of explaining the study findings and putting them in context.

How did the researchers interpret the results?

The researchers say they found "a complex pattern of stresses and adverse events" before the suicides took place.

Of the factors that affect young people specifically, they singled out academic pressures, which they said were often unrecognised at the time, and bullying, which was more often face to face rather than online.

They also point to "suicide-related Internet use", by which they mean searching online for suicide methods or posting suicidal thoughts online, in 25% of people.

Regarding the perhaps surprising finding that physical health conditions were common, they say that acne and asthma, which were most commonly reported, could both lead to social isolation or withdrawing from social activities.

They point out that, "Many of these factors are common in young people in general and on their own cannot be used to predict suicide risk."

They suggest some "long-term" stresses, such as child abuse, substance misuse or mental illness in the family, could be worsened by later experiences such as bereavement or bullying, before a "final straw" pressure such as exam stress or a relationship break-up finally leads to suicide.

They go on to say that this pattern "could offer opportunities to intervene" if society as a whole has a better understanding of the pressures that can lead to a young person taking his or her life.

26 May 2016

⇨ The above information is reprinted with kind permission from NHS Choices. Please visit www.nhs.uk/news/2016/05May/Pages/Exam-stress-linked-to-teen-suicide.aspx for further information.

New study warns of confidence crisis amongst British teenagers

Sky Academy has published extensive new research examining the confidence issues faced by young people in the UK aged 11–24. The findings paint a stark picture of British adolescence as one in three young people surveyed (33%) claim they are not confident.

The study, which was carried out in collaboration with YouGov for Sky Academy, features findings drawn from over 1,600 young people aged between 11–24 years old and 600 parents of children aged 11–24 across the country. In response to the findings, Sky Academy launches a Confidence Month, starting from today (23 September) in a bid to highlight the importance of confidence in young people's development. As part of the campaign, Sky Academy will showcase its initiatives which aim to build practical skills, experience and confidence to unlock the potential of one million young people by 2020.

Confidence is lowest among 17-year-olds

The research identified that by the time young people reach the age of 17, nearly half (45%) claim they are "not confident". The pressures of exams, relationships and defining their identity can have an impact on confidence. At the age of 17, some teenagers also experience increasing levels of self-doubt as they are exposed to a constant tension between wanting to be the same as their friends (49%) and wanting to stand out as an individual (44%).

Despite this decline in confidence, the findings indicate that nearly two in five (37%) social media users aged 14–17 surveyed online feel they can be more confident via these channels than in person. While 31% of young people aged 14–17 claim they can be more honest on social media about issues that worry them. This demonstrates that as young people mature, teenagers prefer to seek support and advice from online followers and friends. However, the use of social media does not necessarily translate into increased confidence in reality, as it only provides a buffer to the outside world.

In contrast to this, the research identified 11-year-olds were the most confident age group in the study (73%). This age group is largely built up by close friends and family, ensuring young people can try new things, practise and voice their opinion in an environment where they will be reassured and encouraged. Receiving supportive feedback was identified as a fundamental factor behind this confidence boost, with 82% of 11-year-olds receiving praise from their parents.

The confidence curve

The findings suggest that as young people mature they go on a confidence journey. Confidence peaks amongst pre-teen children as they have less to worry about and seek external validation from parents, teachers and club activity leaders. The pursuit of self-discovery and facing constant unfamiliar territory at the height of teenage years causes a dip in confidence levels as young people become more worried about how they come across and express themselves in front of others (64%). It is not until young people build life experience and develop a clearer sense of identity in their late teens and early twenties that confidence begins to return.

The confidence gender gap

As part of the nationwide study, the research discovered a noticeable difference between the confidence levels of teenage girls and boys. Despite out-performing boys by 8.4% in the 2015 GCSE results (grades A*–C), girls' confidence levels were still lower than their male counterparts (67% vs 60%). When asked to select what affects their confidence, the biggest factor girls' identified was "appearance" and the "clothes they wear." Over two-thirds (66%) of girls' confidence is influenced by how attractive/unattractive they feel, compared to just 46% of boys.

The gender divide continues as figures reveal that girls are more likely to struggle with new and unfamiliar experiences, which make them feel unconfident. The research found that 61% of girls struggle with confidence

> ## 42% of young people worry about how others perceive them "often" or "all the time"

when starting a first day at school, college or a job, compared to only 46% of boys. These findings suggest that girls prefer to seek protection with familiar people and situations.

Confidence trumps being naturally clever

Figures confirmed that both parents and young people aged 11–24 years old believe confidence is an important factor to achieving life success. Learnt attributes such as communication skills (98% parents, 95% kids), confidence (97% parents, 90% kids) and resilience (96% parents, 91% kids) were identified as more important factors in being successful compared to innate attributes such as being naturally clever (72% parents, 67% kids).

Despite the pressures placed on young people to study and do well at school, 82% of parents surveyed believe "appearance" is a vital element in being successful, while 72% rate being naturally clever as being important.

Parental role in boosting confidence

Throughout the teenage years, parents remain a critical source of support. However, the findings suggest there is a considerable disconnect as parents have an inflated sense of their child's confidence. Overall nearly one in four of parents think their child is not confident, yet the number of kids aged 11–24 saying they lack confidence is one in three Similarly, parents underestimate the impact of certain situations on their child's confidence. While 32% of children say they feel nervous when around peers they believe are popular or attractive, only 9% of parents realise this is an issue for their child. When delving deeper into the findings, mothers and female guardians were identified as being the primary praise-giver (78%) closely followed by friends (74%). Fathers and male guardians were regarded lower with 66% of young people claiming their dads offered them a substantial confidence boost.

Jessica Ennis-Hill, Sky Academy Ambassador comments:

"Nothing is more powerful than confidence. In my career it was my parents who first gave me the encouragement and confidence to overcome boundaries and achieve my goals. It was then about hard work and determination to build the skills I needed to succeed. I'm thrilled to be involved in the Sky Academy Confidence Month and I hope to inspire and encourage a newfound confidence amongst young people."

Annette Du Bois, child confidence expert comments: "Today more than ever before, young people across the UK are feeling emotional imbalance, general insecurity, low self-esteem and a lack of confidence, creating anxiety and mild to excessive unhappiness. The modern and complex world has created the fertile ground upon which emotional and psychological pressures are felt much earlier on. Trying to keep up, gain acceptance or fit in, both online and offline can lead to a decline in well-being, life-skills, and social interaction. By learning effective, easy to apply, purpose-designed tools and techniques to build confidence, young people develop lasting self-belief to reach their full potential in life."

Lucy Carver, Director of the Bigger Picture, Sky, said: "It's clear from these findings and our own research that confidence plays a crucial role in helping young people succeed and unlock their potential. Having worked with over a quarter of million eight- to 24-year-olds so far, we know that by providing real experiences, Sky Academy builds skills which ultimately build confidence. It's our aim to help one million young people by 2020."

Sky Academy Confidence Month

Today, Sky Academy launches a nationwide Confidence Month. The initiative will be supported by a host of ambassadors including Jessica Ennis-Hill, Davina McCall, Alfie Deyes, Sir Chris Hoy, Ella Eyre, Justine Roberts,and Melvyn Bragg. Over the course of the next month, the ambassadors will be taking part in various Sky Academy initiatives up and down the country to engage with young people and share their experiences of how confidence has played a positive role in their career.

18 May 2017

⇨ The above information is reprinted with kind permission from Sky Academy. Please visit www.corporate.sky.com/.../news for further information.

Social interaction
Life skills
Wellbeing

CONFIDENCE CLIMB

Young people's health – the latest trends

Adolescence is a critical time for laying the foundation for health and well-being in adulthood. Overall, statistics for the UK and/or England and Wales show that many of the trends in health behaviours and health outcomes for young people are going in a positive direction, but there are also some more worrying indicators.

Long-term conditions
Rates of non-communicable diseases in this age group are an ongoing concern.

25% of young women

&

14% of young men take prescribed medication

25% of 11–15-year-olds report that they have a long-term illness or disability, including asthma, diabetes, epilepsy and arthritis.

Mental Health
We still lack good, up-to-date prevalence data, but there are some warning signs that trends may not be positive.

In 2014

41,921

young people aged 10–24 were admitted to hospital for self-harm through either cutting, poisoning or other methods

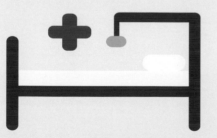

Rates for hospital admissions for self-harm for 10–24-year-olds have risen from 330 per 100,000 in 2007/8, to 367 in 2013/14

75% of mental health problems start before age 24

Referrals to specialist child and adolescent mental health services (CAMHS) increased by 64% between 2012–2015

March 2017

⇨ The above information is reprinted with kind permission from the Association for Young People's Health (AYPH)

⇨ Citation: Association for Young People's Health (2017) *Young people's health, where are we up to?* Updated 2017 London: AYPH.

Report highlights loneliness and lack of social integration amongst young people

⇨ New report into social intelligence by King's College London and National Citizen Service (NCS) identifies a gap in young people's ability to interact with people from different backgrounds

⇨ Developing 'social intelligence' is essential to the economy of the future and in building resilience against loneliness and mental health conditions in later life

⇨ NCS recommends young people find opportunities to develop social intelligence to confidently navigate the workplace and improve well-being

In an increasingly globalised economy and culturally diverse country, a new report from King's College London and NCS reveals a "concerning" lack of social integration and level of loneliness amongst the next generation of young people, which could be harmful to the UK's economy and well-being in the future.

Authored by Dr Jennifer Lau, a researcher specialising in the psychology of adolescent mental health at the Institute of Psychiatry, Psychology & Neuroscience (IoPPN), King's College London, and NCS, the report explores why 'social intelligence', defined as the ability to apply our understanding of people's emotions to decide the appropriate form of interaction with others, will become increasingly important to future generations. The report draws on previous studies and new research amongst employers, adults and young people that identifies how the current generation of young people may require additional support.

It also discusses measures of social intelligence in light of an increasingly diverse, technology-reliant and connected country. Despite criticisms that social media could negatively impact on young people's social skills, the report found that increased online interaction does not damage teenagers' social intelligence levels. The findings showed a small relationship in the opposite direction:

teenagers with better ability to form friendships reported more online usage thus suggesting that online usage could support the development of their social skills.

Dr Jennifer Lau, researcher from King's College London, said: "It is surprising to see that online interaction is positively linked to a young person's social intelligence levels. This could be an indication that young people are using the Internet as a platform to build relationships with others and to practise their social skills.

She added: "However, while important as a means of practising social skills, online interaction is not a substitute for real-life interaction. Not only is online interaction associated with more loneliness in later life – as indicated by our research – this form of communication alone is not adequate in preparing young people for the challenges of the workplace."

Instead, the research shows one of the indicators of lower social skills amongst the next generation is the inability for teenagers to interact with other young people from different backgrounds. With a lack of social integration estimated to cost the UK economy £6 million a year, new research shows more than two-thirds of peer groups are still made up of those from similar backgrounds and nine in ten adolescents are nervous about interacting with people from different backgrounds.

The study recommends social mixing should form an integral part of social intelligence development in teenagers. It argues that parents may have an important role to play, as older generations' own circles also remain relatively closed to different cultures, backgrounds and upbringing.

According to the report, another concerning consequence of low social intelligence levels amongst teenagers is increased loneliness, both in the immediate term and in later life. Despite loneliness being often associated with older people, new research shows six in ten teenagers are sometimes lonely and one in 20 never spend time with friends outside of school. The research indicates that if social intelligence skills aren't developed during adolescence they could lead to loneliness and reduced well-being in later life, making a clear case for social intelligence's role in building resilience against social isolation and mental health conditions in later life.

5 April 2016

⇨ The above information is reprinted with kind permission from Kings's College London. Please visit www.kcl.ac.uk/.../Report-highlights-loneliness-and-lack-of-social-integration-a for further information.

New ESPAD results: teenage drinking and smoking down, but concerns posed by new drugs and new addictive behaviours

Smoking and drinking among 15–16-year-old school students are showing signs of decline, but there are concerns over challenges posed by new drugs and new addictive behaviours. And while overall illicit drug use is stable in this group after previous increases (1995–2003), it continues at high levels. These are among the findings released today in the latest report from the European School Survey Project on Alcohol and Other Drugs (ESPAD). The study, published in collaboration with the EU drugs agency (EMCDDA), is based on a 2015 survey in 35 European countries, including 24 EU Member States.[1]

This is the sixth data-collection wave conducted by the ESPAD project since 1995 (every four years), the latest round coinciding with its 20th anniversary. A total of 96,043 students participated in the survey, responding in school to an anonymous questionnaire. The results, showing 20-year trends, will be presented at the EMCDDA today during the agency's annual expert group meeting on general population surveys.[2]

The ESPAD Report 2015 features information on students' experience of, and perceptions about, a variety of substances including: tobacco, alcohol, illicit drugs, inhalants, pharmaceuticals and new psychoactive substances (NPS). Special attention is given in the new report to NPS, excessive Internet use and online gaming and gambling, all of which were monitored for the first time in this survey round.

The EMCDDA includes ESPAD data in its annual reporting on the drug situation and the two bodies work closely together to enhance understanding of long-term drug use trends among this population in Europe.[3]

Decline in teenage drinking and smoking, but heavy episodic drinking still a concern

Positive developments are seen with regard to teenage smoking across the board (lifetime use, last-30-day use and daily use), against a backdrop of tobacco policy measures introduced over the last two decades.[4] In the 2015 survey, over half of the respondents (54% range: 34% to 84%) reported that they had never smoked, while less than a quarter (21% range: 6% to 37%) reported they were "current smokers" (last 30 days). The proportion of students who started daily smoking at an early age (before 13) decreased over the 20 years: from 10% to 4%. Daily smoking, including early onset of this practice, continues to be more prevalent among boys, but the gender gap has narrowed over the 20 years as it has for smoking overall. Despite strict regulations on tobacco in most countries, over 60% of adolescents still reported relatively easy access to it.

Alcohol use among adolescents in Europe remains high, but here also, time trends since 1995 show some positive developments. Lifetime use of alcohol decreased from 89% to 81% between 1995 and 2015 and last-30-day use from 56% to 47%, with a marked decrease seen in both patterns after a peak in 2003.

The prevalence of "heavy episodic drinking" has remained unchanged over the 20 years, with values in 2015 similar to those in 1995. However, after progressive increases from 1995, the prevalence values decreased clearly from 2011 to 2015 (for boys 44% to 37%; for girls 38% to 33%) in some countries. Less positively, every third student (35%) reported heavy episodic drinking in the past month in the latest survey. Over three-quarters of respondents (78%) reported relatively easy access to alcohol.

Illicit drug use stable, but still at high levels

On average 18% of students reported having used an illicit drug at least once in their life, but levels varied considerably across the ESPAD countries (range: 6%–37%). Following a general upward trend between 1995 and 2003 in the prevalence of illicit drug use, this has remained largely stable since 2003. However, illicit drug use remains at high levels, with ten countries reporting levels in excess of 25%.

The most prevalent illicit drug in all ESPAD countries was cannabis. On average, 16% of the students reported using cannabis at least once in their lifetime (range: 4%–37%). On average, 7% of students had used cannabis in the last 30 days (range: 1%–17%). Between 1995 and 2015, trends in cannabis use indicated a general increase in both lifetime use (11% to 17%) and last-30-day use (4% to 7%).

Prevalence peaked in 2003 (19%) and slightly decreased thereafter (17%).

Around three in ten students (30%) considered cannabis to be easily available. The perceived availability of other illicit drugs was relatively low: ecstasy (12%), cocaine (11%), amphetamine (9%), methamphetamine (7%) and crack (8%).

Across the ESPAD countries, 4% of the students reported lifetime experience with new psychoactive substances (NPS) (range: 1%–10%), while 3% said they had used them in the past year (range: 1%–8%). On average, NPS seem to be more commonly used than amphetamines, ecstasy, cocaine or LSD, all of which have lower lifetime prevalence rates, underlining the need to closely monitor NPS.

Internet use, gaming and gambling – close monitoring needed

With the Internet now an integral part of daily life, "the development of patterns of addictive use among children and adolescents needs to be closely monitored and investigated", states the report. Questions on the amount and purpose of Internet use were included in the latest questionnaire, with a focus on six activities: social media use; information seeking/surfing; streaming/downloading; online gaming; online money gambling and buying/selling.

On average, students used the Internet on 5.8 days per week. Girls used social media regularly more often than boys (four or more days in the last week) (83% versus 73%). Online gaming was more prevalent among boys (39% compared to 7%). In all countries, considerably more boys than girls reported gambling experience in all forms (23% versus 5% on average) or gambling frequently (12% versus 2%) in the last year.

The ESPAD Group expresses concern over the popularity of online gaming and youth gambling: "Measures to prevent adolescents from developing problems associated with gambling, such as debts, psychological deficits and social disadvantages, are of high priority".

EMCDDA Director Alexis Goosdeel said: "For the past 20 years, ESPAD has been providing us with valuable insights into patterns and trends in adolescent substance use across Europe. Now this latest report has extended the scope of the survey to include not only new drugs but also new and potentially addictive behaviours that are raising public concern, such as excessive Internet use, gaming and gambling. By monitoring these new developments, ESPAD is increasing its contribution to protecting adolescents from the negative consequences of substance use and of addictive behaviours in general".

Notes:

1 The report (in English) and the full dataset underpinning the analysis are available online at www.espad.org. Tables can be downloaded in Excel format. All samples were nationally representative, apart from Belgium (Flanders), Cyprus (government controlled areas) and Moldova (Transnistria region not included). ESPAD surveys allow comparisons between participating countries through a common methodology. Under its first ENP technical cooperation project, the EMCDDA co-funded ESPAD 2015 surveys in Georgia, Moldova and Ukraine.

2 For further details on this meeting, see emcdda.europa.eu/meetings/2016/gps

3 Over the last two years, the EMCDDA has scaled up its support for ESPAD and is now a member of its coordination group. For more, see www.emcdda.europa.eu/about/partners/espad – www.emcdda.europa.eu/news/2011/fs-6

4 Policy measures have been implemented in the majority of European countries in the context of the Framework Convention on Tobacco Control (FCTC) over the past two decades (Shibuya, K., Ciecierski, C., Guindon, E., & Bettcher, D. W. (2003). WHO framework convention on tobacco control: development of an evidence based global public health treaty. *British Medical Journal*, 327 (7407), p.154).

14 July 2017

⇨ The above information is reprinted with kind permission from ESPAD. Please visit www.espad.org/news/2016/new-espad-results for further information.

Young people and smoking

Smoking prevalence

It is estimated that each year around 207,000 children in the UK start smoking.[1] Among adult smokers, about two-thirds report that they took up smoking before the age of 18 and over 80% before the age of 20.[2] The 2011 *General Lifestyle Survey* of adult smokers revealed that almost two-fifths (40%) had started smoking regularly before the age of 16.[3]

Among children who try smoking it is estimated that between one-third and one-half are likely to become regular smokers within two to three years.[4]

The annual Government survey of smoking among secondary school pupils in England defines regular smoking as smoking at least one cigarette a week. However, most pupils smoke considerably more than this and in 2014 pupils classified as regular smokers smoked an average (mean) of 31.1 cigarettes a week. Occasional smokers consumed on average five cigarettes a week.[5] The number of cigarettes smoked by regular smokers has fallen significantly since 2007.

The proportion of children who have ever smoked continues to decline. In 2014, 18% of 11–15-year-olds (22% in 2013) had smoked at least once, the lowest proportion since the survey began in 1982 when 53% had tried smoking.[5] In the past decade, the proportion of children who had ever smoked has more than halved from 42% in 2003 to 18% in 2014.[5] The prevalence of regular smoking increases with age, from 0% of 11-year-olds to 8% of 15-year-olds.[5]

Exposure to secondhand smoke

In 2014, nearly two thirds (64%) of pupils reported being exposed to secondhand smoke indoors or in a car. Of these, 59% experienced secondhand smoke in their own or other people's homes and 34% were exposed to smoke in a car.[5]

Use of electronic cigarettes

In 2014, the Smoking, Drinking & Drug Use survey included, for the first time, questions on children's knowledge of, and use of electronic cigarettes. In common with other surveys,[6] this survey found regular use of e-cigarettes to be negligible (1%) and use to be strongly linked to smoking behaviour: 89% of regular smokers reported having tried e-cigarettes compared to only 11% of children who had never smoked. For further information about e-cigarette use among children in Great Britain see ASH Fact Sheet: *Use of electronic cigarettes among children in Great Britain*.

What factors influence children to start smoking?

Smoking initiation is associated with a wide range of risk factors including: parental and sibling smoking, the ease of obtaining cigarettes, smoking by friends and peer group members, socioeconomic status, exposure to tobacco marketing, and depictions of smoking in films, television and other media.[7]

Children who live with parents or siblings who smoke are up to three times more likely to become smokers themselves than children of non-smoking households.[8] It is estimated that, each year, at least 23,000 young people in England and Wales start smoking by the age of 15 as a result of exposure to smoking in the home.[7]

Smoking, alcohol and drug use

There is a strong association between smoking and other substance use. As in previous years, the 2014 secondary school survey found strong overlaps of substance use. Based on those who gave valid responses, among 15-year-olds, 10% reported smoking in the week before the survey, including 9% who had also drunk alcohol or taken drugs recently, or had done both.[5]

Other factors associated with smoking

As in previous surveys, the 2014 survey found that young people who played truant from school or who had been excluded from school in the previous 12 months were almost twice as likely to smoke regularly compared to those who had never been truant or excluded.[5]

Attitudes to smoking

The proportion of pupils who think it is acceptable to try smoking has decreased significantly since the question was first asked in 1999. In 2014, 26% believed it was acceptable to try smoking to see what it is like compared with 54% in 1999, while 10% thought it was OK to try smoking once a week.[5]

Children's beliefs about why people their own age smoke differed according to their own smoking behaviour. Smokers were more likely to believe that young people smoked because of its effects: for example, it helped them cope with stress or relax, or it gave them a positive feeling or helped them stay slim. Non-smokers were more likely to believe that people their age smoked because of social pressures: to look cool in front of friends, because it was exciting to break rules, or because their friends pressured them into it.[5]

Smoking and children's health

The younger the age of uptake of smoking, the greater the harm is likely to be because early uptake is associated with subsequent heavier smoking, higher levels of dependency, a lower chance of quitting, and higher mortality.[7]

Child and adolescent smoking causes serious risks to respiratory health both in the short and long term. Children who smoke are two to six times more susceptible to coughs and increased phlegm, wheeziness and shortness of breath than those who do not smoke.[9] Smoking impairs lung growth and initiates premature lung function decline which may lead to an increased risk of chronic obstructive lung disease later in life. The earlier children become regular smokers and persist in the habit as adults, the greater the risk of developing lung cancer or heart disease.[10]

Children are also more susceptible to the effects of passive smoking. Parental smoking is the main determinant of exposure in non-smoking children. Although levels of exposure in the home

Percentage of regular smokers aged 11–15 by sex: 1982–2014, England[5]

Years	1982	1986	1990	1994	1998	2002	2006	2010	2012	2013	2014
Boys	11	7	9	10	9	9	7	4	4	3	3
Girls	11	12	11	13	12	11	10	6	4	4	4
Total	11	10	10	12	11	10	9	5	4	3	3

Note: ONS estimates that in 2014 around 90,000 children aged 11–15 were regular smokers (CI=80,000–110,000); about 10,000 fewer than in 2013.

The decline in smoking has been most marked among older pupils. The proportion of 14-year-olds who smoked regularly fell from 13% in 2006 to 4% in 2013 (and 2014); among 15-year-olds, 8% smoked regularly in 2014, compared with 20% in 2006.[5]

Percentage of 15-year-old regular smokers: 1982–2014, England[5]

Years	1982	1986	1990	1994	1998	2002	2006	2010	2012	2013	2014
Boys	24	18	25	26	19	20	16	10	10	8	6
Girls	25	27	25	30	29	26	24	14	10	8	9
Total	25	22	25	28	24	23	20	12	10	8	8

have declined in the UK in recent years, children living in the poorest households have the highest levels of exposure as measured by cotinine, a marker for nicotine.[11]

Bronchitis, pneumonia, asthma and sudden infant death syndrome (cot death) are significantly more common in infants and children who have one or two smoking parents.[11] For more information see the ASH Research Report: *Passive smoking: the impact on children*, ASH Factsheets: *Secondhand smoke in the Home, and Smoking in Cars.*

Addiction

Children who experiment with cigarettes can quickly become addicted to the nicotine in tobacco. Children may show signs of addiction within four weeks of starting to smoke and before they commence daily smoking.[12] One US study[13] found that smoking just one cigarette in early childhood doubled the chance of a teenager becoming a regular smoker by the age of 17 and a London study suggests that smoking a single cigarette is a risk indicator for children to become regular smokers up to three years later.[14]

In the 2014 survey of school-children in England, 53% of young people who had smoked for under one year say they would find it difficult to stop for one week compared to 85% for those who have smoked more than one year.[5] The survey also found that 29% of regular smokers said that they wanted to give up smoking, while 56% reported that they had tried to give up.

During periods of abstinence, young people experience withdrawal symptoms similar to the kind experienced by adult smokers. [9,15]

Smoking prevention

Research suggests that knowledge about smoking is a necessary component of anti-smoking campaigns but by itself does not affect smoking rates. It may, however, result in a postponement of initiation.[16] High prices can deter children from smoking, since young people do not possess a large disposable income: studies suggest young people may be up to three to four times more price sensitive than adults.[17]

In Canada, when cigarette prices were raised dramatically in the 1980s and the early 1990s youth consumption of tobacco plummeted by 60%.[18] An American study has shown that while price does not appear to affect initial experimentation of smoking, it is an important tool in reducing youth smoking once the habit has become established.[19]

The National Institute for Health and Care Excellence (NICE) has issued guidance on school-based interventions to prevent the uptake of smoking among children.[20]

Children, smoking and the law

On 1 October 2007 the legal age for the purchase of tobacco in England and Wales was raised from 16 to18. The measure was designed to make it more difficult for teenagers to obtain cigarettes, since, despite the law, children still succeeded in buying tobacco from shops and vending machines.

In 2008, the first time data were collected after the change in the law, 39% of pupils who smoked said they found it difficult to buy cigarettes from shops, an increase of 15% from 24% in 2006.[21] There has also been a drop in the proportion of regular smokers who usually buy their cigarettes from a shop: from 78% in 2006 to 57% in 2014.[5]

Other measures designed to deter children from smoking include a ban on the sale of cigarettes from vending machines which entered into force in England on 1 October 2011 and a ban on the display of tobacco products in retail outlets.[22]

During 2013 there were 98 prosecutions in England and Wales for underage tobacco sales, with 78 defendants being found guilty.[23] An amendment to the Criminal Justice and Immigration Act includes banning orders for retailers who persistently sell tobacco to persons under the age of 18. This measure came into force in April 2009.

In February 2014, Parliament passed an amendment to the Children and Families Bill allowing the Government to introduce regulations making it an offence to smoke in a private vehicle carrying children. This measure will enter into force on 1 October 2015 and will apply to England and Wales.

Three other amendments were passed enabling the Government to introduce regulations:

- requiring standardised packaging for tobacco products (throughout the UK),

- making it an offence to sell e-cigarettes to children under 18 – (England and Wales)

- making it an offence for an adult to buy cigarettes for anyone under 18 – proxy purchasing (England and Wales).

Standardised packaging is due to enter into force in May 2016 and the regulations on proxy purchasing and prohibiting the sale of e-cigarettes to under-18s will commence on 1 October 2015.

Legislation alone is not sufficient to prevent tobacco sales to minors. Both enforcement and community policies may improve compliance by retailers but the impact on underage smoking prevalence using these approaches alone may still be small.[24] Successful efforts to limit underage access to tobacco require a combination of approaches that tackle the problem comprehensively.

References

1 Hopkinson, NS., Lester-George, A., Ormiston-Smith, N., Cox, A. & Arnott, D. Child uptake of smoking by area across the UK. Thorax 2013. doi:10.1136/thoraxjnl-2013-204379

2 Robinson S & Bugler C. Smoking and drinking among adults, 2008. General Lifestyle Survey 2008. ONS, 2010.

3 Office for National Statistics. General Lifestyle Survey Overview: A report on the 2011 General Lifestyle Survey. 2013.

4 Harm reduction in nicotine reduction. Helping people who can't quit. A report of the Tobacco Advisory Group of the Royal College of Physicians, London, RCP, 2007.

5 Smoking drinking and drug use among young people in England in 2014. Health & Social Care Information Centre, 2015.

6 Health Survey for England, 2013. Scottish Schools Adolescent Lifestyle and Substance Use Survey (SALSUS) 2013; ASH fact sheet: Use of electronic cigarettes among children in Great Britain.

7 Passive smoking and children. Royal College of Physicians, London, 2010 (pdf).

8 Leonardi-Bee J, Jere ML, Britton J. Exposure to parental and sibling smoking and the risk of smoking uptake in childhood and adolsecence: a systematic review and meta-analysis. Thorax 15 Feb. 2011 doi:10.1136/thx.2010.153379.

9 Smoking and the Young. Royal College of Physicians, 1992.

10 BMA Board of Science. Breaking the cycle of children's exposure to tobacco smoke. British Medical Association, London, 2007.

11 Going smoke-free. The medical case for clean air in the home, at work and in public places. A

report on passive smoking by the Tobacco Advisory Group of the Royal College of Physicians. London, Royal College of Physicians, 2005.

12 Di Franza JR et al. Initial symptoms of nicotine addiction in adolescents. Tobacco Control 2000; 9: 313-319.

13 Jackson, C & Dickinson, D. Cigarette consumption during childhood and persistence of smoking through adolescence. Arch Pediatr Adolesc Med. 2004;158: 1050-1056.

14 Fidler, JA et al Vulnerability to smoking after trying a single cigarette can lie dormant for three years or more. Tobacco control 2006; 15: 205-209.

15 Nicotine addiction in Britain. A report of the Tobacco Advisory Group of the Royal College of Physicians. London, RCP, 2000.

16 Reid D. et al. Reducing the prevalence of smoking in youth in Western countries: an international review. Tobacco Control 1995; 4 (3): 266 - 277 (pdf).

17 Hopkins, D et al. Reviews of evidence regarding interventions to reduce tobacco use and exposure to environmental tobacco smoke. Am J Prev Med 2001; 20: 16-66

18 Sweanor, D and Martial LR, The Smuggling of tobacco products: Lessons from Canada. (Non-Smokers Rights Association, 1994).

19 Emery, S. White, M and Pierce, J. Does cigarette price influence adolescent experimentation? J Health Economics 2001; 20: 261–270.

20 School-based interventions to prevent the uptake of smoking among children. NICE, March 2010 .

21 Smoking, drinking and drug use among young people in England in 2008. The Information Centre for Health and Social Care, 2009.

22 Health Act 2009.

23 Number of defendants cautioned, proceeded against at magistrates' courts and found guilty and sentenced at all courts for selling tobacco to underage persons, England and Wales, 2010 and 2011.
Justice Statistics Analytical Services, 2013.

24 Lancaster T, Stead LF. Interventions for preventing tobacco sales to minors. (Review) The Cochrane Library, 2008, Issue 3.

July 2015

⇨ The above information is reprinted with kind permission from ASH. Please visit www.ash.org.uk/information-and-resources/fact-sheets/young-people-and-smoking for further information.

Iceland knows how to stop teen substance abuse but the rest of the world isn't listening

In Iceland, teenage smoking, drinking and drug use have been radically cut in the past 20 years. Emma Young finds out how they did it, and why other countries won't follow suit.

By Emma Young

It's a little before three on a sunny Friday afternoon and Laugardalur Park, near central Reykjavik, looks practically deserted. There's an occasional adult with a pushchair, but the park's surrounded by apartment blocks and houses, and school's out – so where are all the kids?

Walking with me are Gudberg Jónsson, a local psychologist, and Harvey Milkman, an American psychology professor who teaches for part of the year at Reykjavik University. 20 years ago, says Gudberg, Icelandic teens were among the heaviest drinking youths in Europe. "You couldn't walk the streets in downtown Reykjavik on a Friday night because it felt unsafe," adds Milkman. "There were hordes of teenagers getting in-your-face drunk."

We approach a large building. "And here we have the indoor skating," says Gudberg.

A couple of minutes ago, we passed two halls dedicated to badminton and ping pong. Here in the park, there's also an athletics track, a geothermally heated swimming pool and – at last – some visible kids, excitedly playing football on an artificial pitch.

Young people aren't hanging out in the park right now, Gudberg explains, because they're in after-school classes in these facilities, or in clubs for music, dance or art. Or they might be on outings with their parents.

Today, Iceland tops the European table for the cleanest-living teens. The percentage of 15- and 16-year-olds who had been drunk in the previous month plummeted from 42 per cent in 1998 to five per cent in 2016. The percentage who have ever used cannabis is down from 17 per cent to seven per cent. Those smoking cigarettes every day fell from 23 per cent to just three per cent.

The way the country has achieved this turnaround has been both radical and evidence-based, but it has relied a lot on what might be termed enforced common sense "This is the most remarkably intense and profound study of stress in the lives of teenagers that I have ever seen," says Milkman. "I'm just so impressed by how well it is working."

If it was adopted in other countries, Milkman argues, the Icelandic model could benefit the general psychological and physical well-being of millions of kids, not to mention the coffers of healthcare agencies and broader society. It's a big if.

"I was in the eye of the storm of the drug revolution," Milkman explains over tea in his apartment in Reykjavik. In the early 1970s, when he was doing an internship at the Bellevue Psychiatric Hospital in New York City, "LSD was already in, and a lot of people were smoking marijuana. And there was a lot of interest in why people took certain drugs."

Milkman's doctoral dissertation concluded that people would choose either heroin or amphetamines depending on how they liked to deal with stress. Heroin users wanted to numb themselves; amphetamine users wanted to actively confront it. After this work was published, he was among a group of researchers drafted by the US National Institute on Drug Abuse to answer questions such as: why do people start using drugs? Why do they continue? When do they reach a threshold to abuse? When do they stop? And when do they relapse?

"Any college kid could say: why do they start? Well, there's availability, they're risk-takers, alienation, maybe some depression," he says. "But why do they continue? So I got to the question about the threshold for abuse and the lights went on – that's when I had my version of the 'aha' experience: they could be on the threshold for abuse before they even took the drug, because it was their style of coping that they were abusing."

At Metropolitan State College of Denver, Milkman was instrumental in developing the idea that people were getting addicted to changes in brain chemistry. Kids who were "active confronters" were after a rush – they'd get it by stealing hubcaps and radios and later cars, or through stimulant drugs. Alcohol also alters brain chemistry, of course. It's a sedative but it sedates the brain's control first, which can remove inhibitions and, in limited doses, reduce anxiety.

"People can get addicted to drink, cars, money, sex, calories, cocaine – whatever," says Milkman. "The idea of behavioural addiction became our trademark."

This idea spawned another: "Why not orchestrate a social movement around natural highs: around people getting high on their own brain chemistry – because it seems obvious to me that people want to change their consciousness – without the deleterious effects of drugs?"

By 1992, his team in Denver had won a $1.2m government grant to form Project Self-Discovery, which offered teenagers natural-high alternatives to drugs and crime. They got referrals from teachers, school nurses and counsellors, taking in kids from the age of 14 who didn't see themselves as needing treatment but who had problems with drugs or petty crime.

"We didn't say to them, you're coming in for treatment. We said, we'll teach you anything you want to learn: music, dance, hip hop, art, martial arts." The idea was that these different classes could provide a variety of alterations in the kids' brain chemistry, and give them what they needed to cope better with life: some might crave an experience that could help reduce anxiety, others may be after a rush.

At the same time, the recruits got life-skills training, which focused on improving their thoughts about

themselves and their lives, and the way they interacted with other people. "The main principle was that drug education doesn't work because nobody pays attention to it. What is needed are the life skills to act on that information," Milkman says. Kids were told it was a three-month programme. Some stayed five years.

In 1991, Milkman was invited to Iceland to talk about this work, his findings and ideas. He became a consultant to the first residential drug treatment centre for adolescents in Iceland, in a town called Tindar. "It was designed around the idea of giving kids better things to do," he explains. It was here that he met Gudberg, who was then a psychology undergraduate and a volunteer at Tindar. They have been close friends ever since.

Milkman started coming regularly to Iceland and giving talks. These talks, and Tindar, attracted the attention of a young researcher at the University of Iceland, called Inga Dóra Sigfúsdóttir. She wondered: what if you could use healthy alternatives to drugs and alcohol as part of a programme not to treat kids with problems, but to stop kids drinking or taking drugs in the first place?

Have you ever tried alcohol? If so, when

did you last have a drink? Have you ever been drunk? Have you tried cigarettes? If so, how often do you smoke? How much time to you spend with your parents? Do you have a close relationship with your parents? What kind of activities do you take part in?

In 1992, 14-, 15- and 16-year-olds in every school in Iceland filled in a questionnaire with these kinds of questions. This process was then repeated in 1995 and 1997.

The results of these surveys were alarming. Nationally, almost 25 per cent were smoking every day, over 40 per cent had got drunk in the past month. But when the team drilled right down into the data, they could identify precisely which schools had the worst problems – and which had the least. Their analysis revealed clear differences between the lives of kids who took up drinking, smoking and other drugs, and those who didn't. A few factors emerged as strongly protective: participation in organised activities – especially sport – three or four times a week, total time spent with parents during the week, feeling cared about at school, and not being outdoors in the late evenings.

"At that time, there had been all kinds of substance prevention efforts and programmes," says Inga Dóra, who was a research assistant on the surveys. "Mostly they were built on education." Kids were being warned about the dangers of drink and drugs, but, as Milkman had observed in the US, these programmes were not working. "We wanted to come up with a different approach."

The mayor of Reykjavik, too, was interested in trying something new, and many parents felt the same, adds Jón Sigfússon, Inga Dóra's colleague and brother. Jón had young daughters at the time and joined her new Icelandic Centre for Social Research and Analysis when it was set up in 1999. "The situation was bad," he says. "It was obvious something had to be done."

Using the survey data and insights from research including Milkman's, a new national plan was gradually introduced. It was called Youth in Iceland.

Laws were changed. It became illegal to buy tobacco under the age of 18 and alcohol under the age of 20, and tobacco and alcohol advertising was

banned. Links between parents and school were strengthened through parental organisations which by law had to be established in every school, along with school councils with parent representatives. Parents were encouraged to attend talks on the importance of spending a quantity of time with their children rather than occasional "quality time", on talking to their kids about their lives, on knowing who their kids were friends with, and on keeping their children home in the evenings.

A law was also passed prohibiting children aged between 13 and 16 from being outside after 10pm in winter and midnight in summer. It's still in effect today.

Home and School, the national umbrella body for parental organisations, introduced agreements for parents to sign. The content varies depending on the age group, and individual organisations can decide what they want to include. For kids aged 13 and up, parents can pledge to follow all the recommendations, and also, for example, not to allow their kids to have unsupervised parties, not to buy alcohol for minors, and to keep an eye on the well-being of other children.

These agreements educate parents but also help to strengthen their authority in the home, argues Hrefna Sigurjónsdóttir, director of Home and School. "Then it becomes harder to use the oldest excuse in the book: 'But everybody else can!'"

State funding was increased for organised sport, music, art, dance and other clubs, to give kids alternative ways to feel part of a group, and to feel good, rather than through using alcohol and drugs, and kids from low-income families received help to take part. In Reykjavik, for instance, where more than a third of the country's population lives, a Leisure Card gives families 35,000 krona (£250) per year per child to pay for recreational activities.

Crucially, the surveys have continued. Each year, almost every child in Iceland completes one. This means up-to-date, reliable data is always available.

Between 1997 and 2012, the percentage of kids aged 15 and 16 who reported often or almost always spending time with their parents on weekdays doubled – from 23 per cent to 46 per cent – and

the percentage who participated in organised sports at least four times a week increased from 24 per cent to 42 per cent. Meanwhile, cigarette smoking, drinking and cannabis use in this age group plummeted.

"Although this cannot be shown in the form of a causal relationship – which is a good example of why primary prevention methods are sometimes hard to sell to scientists – the trend is very clear," notes Álfgeir Kristjánsson, who worked on the data and is now at the West Virginia University School of Public Health in the US. "Protective factors have gone up, risk factors down, and substance use has gone down – and more consistently in Iceland than in any other European country."

Jón Sigfússon apologises for being just a couple of minutes late. "I was on a crisis call!" He prefers not to say precisely to where, but it was to one of the cities elsewhere in the world that has now adopted, in part, the Youth in Iceland ideas.

Youth in Europe, which Jón heads, began in 2006 after the already-remarkable Icelandic data was presented at a European Cities Against Drugs meeting and, he recalls, "People asked: what are you doing?"

Participation in Youth in Europe is at a municipal level rather than being led by national governments. In the first year, there were eight municipalities. To date, 35 have taken part, across 17 countries, varying from some areas where just a few schools take part to Tarragona in Spain, where 4,200 15-year-olds are involved. The method is always the same: Jón and his team talk to local officials and devise a questionnaire with the same core questions as those used in Iceland plus any locally tailored extras. For example, online gambling has recently emerged as a big problem in a few areas, and local officials want to know if it's linked to other risky behaviour.

Just two months after the questionnaires are returned to Iceland, the team sends back an initial report with the results, plus information on how they compare with other participating regions. "We always say that, like vegetables, information has to be fresh," says Jón. "If you bring these findings a year later, people would say,

Oh, this was a long time ago and maybe things have changed…" As well as fresh, it has to be local so that schools, parents and officials can see exactly what problems exist in which areas.

The team has analysed 99,000 questionnaires from places as far afield as the Faroe Islands, Malta and Romania – as well as South Korea and, very recently, Nairobi and Guinea-Bissau. Broadly, the results show that when it comes to teen substance use, the same protective and risk factors identified in Iceland apply everywhere. There are some differences: in one location (in a country "on the Baltic Sea"), participation in organised sport actually emerged as a risk factor. Further investigation revealed that this was because young ex-military men who were keen on muscle-building drugs, drinking and smoking were running the clubs. Here, then, was a well-defined, immediate, local problem that could be addressed.

While Jón and his team offer advice and information on what has been found to work in Iceland, it's up to individual communities to decide what to do in the light of their results. Occasionally, they do nothing. One predominantly Muslim country, which he prefers not to identify, rejected the data because it revealed an unpalatable level of alcohol consumption. In other cities – such as the origin of Jón's "crisis call" – there is an openness to the data and there is money, but he has observed that it can be much more difficult to secure and maintain funding for health prevention strategies than for treatments.

No other country has made changes on the scale seen in Iceland. When asked if anyone has copied the laws to keep children indoors in the evening, Jón smiles. "Even Sweden laughs and calls it the child curfew!"

Across Europe, rates of teen alcohol and drug use have generally improved over the past 20 years, though nowhere as dramatically as in Iceland, and the reasons for improvements are not necessarily linked to strategies that foster teen well-being. In the UK, for example, the fact that teens are now spending more time at home interacting online rather than in person could be one of the major reasons for the drop in alcohol consumption.

But Kaunas, in Lithuania, is one example of what can happen through active intervention. Since 2006, the city has administered the questionnaires five times, and schools, parents, healthcare organisations, churches, the police and social services have come together to try to improve kids' wellbeing and curb substance use. For instance, parents get eight or nine free parenting sessions each year, and a new programme provides extra funding for public institutions and NGOs working in mental health promotion and stress management. In 2015, the city started offering free sports activities on Mondays, Wednesdays and Fridays, and there are plans to introduce a free ride service for low-income families, to help kids who don't live close to the facilities to attend.

Between 2006 and 2014, the number of 15- and 16-year-olds in Kaunas who reported getting drunk in the past 30 days fell by about a quarter, and daily smoking fell by more than 30 per cent.

At the moment, participation in Youth in Europe is a haphazard affair, and the team in Iceland is small. Jón would like to see a centralised body with its own dedicated funding to focus on the expansion of Youth in Europe. "Even though we have been doing this for ten years, it is not our full, main job. We would like somebody to copy this and maintain it all over Europe," he says. "And why only Europe?"

After our walk through Laugardalur Park, Gudberg Jónsson invites us back to his home. Outside, in the garden, his two elder sons, Jón Konrád, who's 21, and Birgir Ísar, who's 15, talk to me about drinking and smoking. Jón does drink alcohol, but Birgir says he doesn't know anyone at his school who smokes or drinks. We also talk about football training: Birgir trains five or six times a week; Jón, who is in his first year of a business degree at the University of Iceland, trains five times a week. They both started regular after-school training when they were six years old.

"We have all these instruments at home," their father told me earlier. "We tried to get them into music. We used to have a horse. My wife is really into horse riding. But it didn't happen. In the end, soccer was their selection."

Did it ever feel like too much? Was there pressure to train when they'd rather have been doing something else? "No, we just had fun playing football," says Birgir. Jón adds, "We tried it and got used to it, and so we kept on doing it."

It's not all they do. While Gudberg and his wife Thórunn don't consciously plan for a certain number of hours each week with their three sons, they do try to take them regularly to the movies, the theatre, restaurants, hiking, fishing and, when Iceland's sheep are brought down from the highlands each September, even on family sheep-herding outings.

Jón and Birgir may be exceptionally keen on football, and talented (Jón has been offered a soccer scholarship to the Metropolitan State University of Denver, and a few weeks after we meet, Birgir is selected to play for the under-17 national team). But could the significant rise in the percentage of kids who take part in organised sport four or more times a week be bringing benefits beyond raising healthier children?

Could it, for instance, have anything to do with Iceland's crushing defeat of England in the Euro 2016 football championship? When asked, Inga Dóra Sigfúsdóttir, who was voted Woman of the Year in Iceland in 2016, smiles: "There is also the success in music, like Of Monsters and Men [an indie folk-pop group from Reykjavik]. These are young people who have been pushed into organised work. Some people have thanked me," she says, with a wink.

Elsewhere, cities that have joined Youth in Europe are reporting other benefits. In Bucharest, for example, the rate of teen suicides is dropping alongside use of drink and drugs. In Kaunas, the number of children committing crimes dropped by a third between 2014 and 2015.

As Inga Dóra says: "We learned through the studies that we need to create circumstances in which kids can lead healthy lives, and they do not need to use substances, because life is fun, and they have plenty to do – and they are supported by parents who will spend time with them."

When it comes down to it, the messages – if not necessarily the methods – are straightforward. And when he looks at the results, Harvey Milkman thinks of his own country, the US. Could the Youth in Iceland model work there, too?

325 million people versus 330,000. 33,000 gangs versus virtually none. Around 1.3 million homeless young people versus a handful.

Clearly, the US has challenges that Iceland does not. But the data from other parts of Europe, including cities such as Bucharest with major social problems and relative poverty, shows that the Icelandic model can work in very different cultures, Milkman argues. And the need in the US is high: underage drinking accounts for about 11 per cent of all alcohol consumed nationwide, and excessive drinking causes more than 4,300 deaths among under-21-year-olds every year.

A national programme along the lines of Youth in Iceland is unlikely to be introduced in the US, however. One major obstacle is that while in Iceland there is long-term commitment to the national project, community health programmes in the US are usually funded by short-term grants.

Milkman has learned the hard way that even widely applauded, gold-standard youth programmes aren't always expanded, or even sustained. "With Project Self-Discovery, it seemed like we had the best programme in the world," he says. "I was invited to the White House twice. It won national awards. I was thinking: this will be replicated in every town and village. But it wasn't."

He thinks that is because you can't prescribe a generic model to every community because they don't all have the same resources. Any move towards giving kids in the US the opportunities to participate in the kinds of activities now common in Iceland, and so helping them to stay away from alcohol and other drugs, will depend on building on what already exists. "You have to rely on the resources of the community," he says.

His colleague Álfgeir Kristjánsson is introducing the Icelandic ideas to the state of West Virginia. Surveys are being given to kids at several middle and high schools in the state, and a community coordinator will help get the results out to parents and anyone else who could use them to help local kids. But it might be difficult

to achieve the kinds of results seen in Iceland, he concedes.

Short-termism also impedes effective prevention strategies in the UK, says Michael O'Toole, CEO of Mentor, a charity that works to reduce alcohol and drug misuse in children and young people. Here, too, there is no national coordinated alcohol and drug prevention programme. It's generally left to local authorities or to schools, which can often mean kids are simply given information about the dangers of drugs and alcohol – a strategy that, he agrees, evidence shows does not work.

O'Toole fully endorses the Icelandic focus on parents, school and the community all coming together to help support kids, and on parents or carers being engaged in young people's lives. Improving support for kids could help in so many ways, he stresses. Even when it comes just to alcohol and smoking, there is plenty of data to show that the older a child is when they have their first drink or cigarette, the healthier they will be over the course of their life.

But not all the strategies would be acceptable in the UK – the child curfews being one, parental walks around neighbourhoods to identify children breaking the rules perhaps another. And

a trial run by Mentor in Brighton that involved inviting parents into schools for workshops found that it was difficult to get them engaged.

Public wariness and an unwillingness to engage will be challenges wherever the Icelandic methods are proposed, thinks Milkman, and go to the heart of the balance of responsibility between states and citizens. "How much control do you want the Government to have over what happens with your kids? Is this too much of the Government meddling in how people live their lives?"

In Iceland, the relationship between people and the state has allowed an effective national programme to cut the rates of teenagers smoking and drinking to excess – and, in the process, brought families closer and helped kids to become healthier in all kinds of ways. Will no other country decide that these benefits are worth the costs?

17 January 2017

⇨ The above information is reprinted with kind permission from *The Independent*. Please visit www.independent.co.uk for further information.

What we know about young people in alcohol and drug treatment

This week PHE has published two important documents about young people's sub-stance misuse.

The first is the 2015–16 annual report, which provides data on young people's use of specialist substance misuse treatment services, which form part of the National Drug Treatment Monitoring System (NDTMS).

The second, a rapid mixed methods evidence review, commissioned by PHE and undertaken by The Children's Society, is a review of young people's specialist substance misuse services. This will help commissioners improve these services.

The annual report shows that the numbers of young people seeking treatment for problems with drugs and alcohol (17,000) continues to decline, since a peak in the numbers in 2008–09 (24,000).

While this is encouraging, and is in line with what we know about the declining use of drugs and alcohol among young people, we need to look behind the headline to understand the full picture.

Young people do not develop substance misuse problems in isolation. The 2015–16 data shows that a significant proportion of young people who entered specialist treatment services also had other multiple problems or vulnerabilities that were linked to their substance misuse. These include:

⇨ having a mental health problem

⇨ being affected by domestic violence or sexual exploitation

⇨ not being in education, training or employment.

For some young people these wider issues may be the cause of their substance misuse problems, and for others, a consequence. So it is vitally important that young people's treatment services are working closely with a wide range of other children and young people's health and social care services, to ensure that vulnerable young people have all their needs supported.

These young people are already at a significant disadvantage in life and, without effective joined-up support, there is a very real risk that their lives get derailed and they may continue to use drugs into adulthood.

Young males and females come into treatment services with different vulnerabilities and so require different responses:

⇨ 6% of young people who seek alcohol and drug treatment report having been sexually exploited, but this is much higher among females (14%) compared to just over 1% of males

⇨ 17% of young people starting treatment in 2015–16 report having self-harmed, with the proportion of females (33%) significantly higher than males (9%)

⇨ 25% of females starting treatment reported having mental health problems, compared to 15% of males.

Cannabis and alcohol continue to be the main substances for which young people seek help. Since the NDTMS started to collect data on new psychoactive substances (NPS) in 2013–14, we have not seen the increase in numbers of young people coming into treatment for problems with NPS that we might have expected.

Over the past year, 2015–16, 6% of young people reported having problems with these substances, compared to 5% in 2014–15. Specialist services need to ensure that they are both easily accessible and equipped to work with young people with a range of problem substances, including NPS.

Waiting times for young people's treatment during 2015–16 continued to be low, which demonstrates the clear recognition that easy access and prompt provision of treatment for young people is vital and a priority for this extremely vulnerable group of young people in England.

The review of specialist services highlights some important principles for local authority commissioners. Essentially:

⇨ young people and their needs should be at the centre of services

⇨ quality governance arrangements should be in place

⇨ multiple vulnerabilities and complex needs should be properly addressed

⇨ young people becoming young adults need to be supported as they move into adult services through appropriate transitional arrangements.

It is encouraging that the numbers of young people being treated for substance misuse is going down. However, it is important to emphasise the complex vulnerabilities experienced by this group and the need to ensure that treatment services are effectively joined up with other young people's health and social care services.

The review provides important advice and we encourage commissioners of young people's treatment services to read in conjunction with the 2015–16 annual report.

12 January 2017

⇨ The above information is reprinted with kind permission from GOV.UK. Please visit www.publichealthmatters.blog.gov.uk

One in seven 11-year-olds have tried alcohol according to new study

Researchers from University College London (UCL) and the London School of Economics have found that nearly 14% of 11-year-olds had drunk more than a few sips of alcohol at least once.

Children whose mothers drank heavily were 80% more likely to drink than children whose mothers did not drink and boys were more likely to report drinking than girls.

Children whose friends drank were five times more likely to drink than those whose friends did not drink. The researchers, who analysed data on more than 10,000 children taking part in the Millennium Cohort Study, also found that friends' drinking had a stronger association with children's alcohol consumption than parents' drinking.

Lead author, Professor Yvonne Kelly, from University College London, explains: "Drinking in adolescence is considered a 'risky' behaviour, it often co-occurs with other 'risky' behaviours and it is linked to educational failure and to premature mortality, for example, via accidental deaths.

"Improving our understanding of the factors that influence drinking is important as it has implications for the development of policies and interventions aimed at reducing 'risky' behaviours."

Other factors associated with drinking were having started puberty, being a second or later born child, having socioemotional difficulties (e.g. sustaining positive relationships, experiencing, managing or expressing emotions) and antisocial behaviours.

The study is thought to be the first to examine drinking behaviours in very early adolescence in relation to a wide range of factors that are associated with alcohol consumption in children, such as family, friends and the young person's views about alcohol.

The researchers suggest that while the vast majority of children at the age of eleven are yet to explore alcohol, investigating in more detail the context in which children drink – who they drink with, where, when, what they drink and how they acquire alcohol – could help inform effective policy and alcohol harm prevention strategies to reduce the risk associated with drinking in youth.

"Our findings support the need for interventions working at multiple levels, including family and school, to help shape choices around risky behaviours including drinking," Professor Kelly concludes.

Further information

'What influences 11-year-olds to drink? Findings from the Millennium Cohort Study', Yvonne Kelly, Alice Goisis, Amanda Sacker, Noriko Cable, Richard G Watt, Annie Britton, is published in BMC Public Health

9 March 2016

⇨ The above information is reprinted with kind permission from the Centre for Longitudinal Studies. Please visit www. cls.ioe.ac.uk for further information.

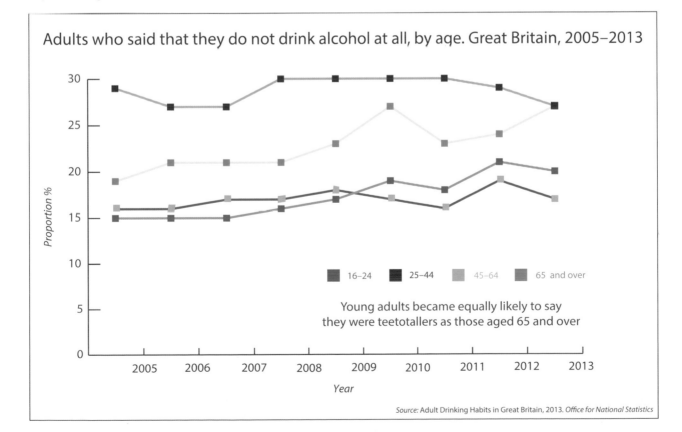

Adults who said that they do not drink alcohol at all, by age. Great Britain, 2005–2013

16–24   25–44   45–64   65 and over

Young adults became equally likely to say they were teetotallers as those aged 65 and over

Source: Adult Drinking Habits in Great Britain, 2013. *Office for National Statistics*

Use of electronic cigarettes among children in Great Britain

Key findings

- Although children's awareness of and experimentation with electronic cigarettes is increasing, regular use remains rare and is most common among those who currently smoke or have previously smoked. This indicates that it is unlikely that electronic cigarettes are currently acting as a gateway to smoking.

- A growing proportion of young people believe that electronic cigarettes are as harmful as smoking tobacco.

- Rechargeable tanks and fruit flavours are the most popular types of e-cigarettes among young people both for experimentation and regular use.

Electronic cigarette use among young people in Great Britain

From 2013 onwards YouGov has been commissioned by ASH to conduct an annual online survey of young people aged between 11 and 18, called Smokefree GB Youth Survey. It includes questions on electronic cigarettes. The most recent Smokefree GB Youth Survey was carried out in March 2016[1] and relevant comparisons with previous years[2][3][4] are presented here.

In 2015 only 7% of 11–18-year-olds said they had not heard of electronic cigarettes, down from 33% in 2013. 13% of those surveyed had tried e-cigarettes at least once, this is up from 5% in 2013. In 2015 more young people (21%) had tried cigarettes than electronic cigarettes and 64% of those using e-cigarettes had tried tobacco first.

Regular use (once a month or more) was rare and largely among children who currently or have previously smoked.

1. Total sample size was 2,331 11- to 18-year-olds. Fieldwork was undertaken between 11 March and 10 April 2016. The survey was carried out online. The figures have been weighted and are representative of all GB 11-18-year-olds

2. Total sample size was 2,291 teenagers aged 11–18. Fieldwork was undertaken between 6 and 22 March 2015. The survey was carried out online. The figures have been weighted and are representative of GB 11–18-year-olds.

3. Total sample size was 2,068 children aged 11–18. Fieldwork was undertaken between 21 March–1 April 2014. The survey was carried out online. The figures have been weighted and are representative of age, gender and region.

4. Total sample size was 2,178 children aged 11 to 18. Fieldwork was undertaken between 21st - 28th March 2013. The survey was carried out online. The figures have been weighted and are representative of all GB aged 11 to 18.

2.4% of respondents said they used electronic cigarettes once a month or more, including 0.5% who used them weekly.

Understanding of electronic cigarettes among children is generally good. Two-thirds of children who have heard of electronic cigarettes believe correctly that they are less harmful than cigarettes to the user (67%) although this has fallen over time, with increasing numbers of children believing they are equally harmful. Between 2013 and 2015 the proportion believing that the electronic devices are as equally as harmful increased from 11% to 21%.

The most popular form of electronic-cigarettes among children are those with a rechargeable tank (34%), followed by those with a pre-filled cartridge (30%). These figures include those who had only tried e-cigarettes once or twice.

E-cigarettes come in a variety of flavours, particularly refillable 'tank' devices. Fruit flavour was by far the most popular flavour among young people. Fruit flavours were more popular among young people who no longer used electronic cigarettes and among young people who had tried electronic cigarettes but never smoked.

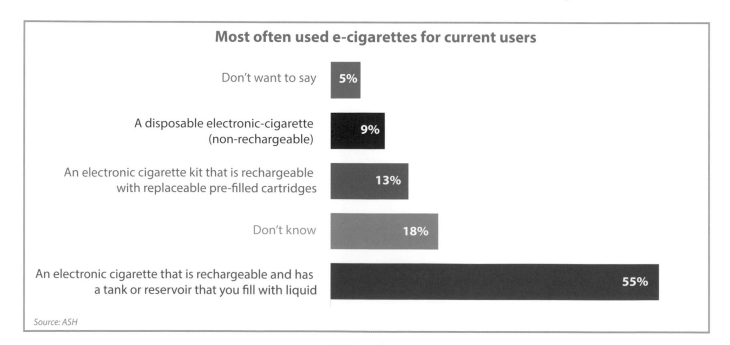

Most often used e-cigarettes for current users

- Don't want to say — 5%
- A disposable electronic-cigarette (non-rechargeable) — 9%
- An electronic cigarette kit that is rechargeable with replaceable pre-filled cartridges — 13%
- Don't know — 18%
- An electronic cigarette that is rechargeable and has a tank or reservoir that you fill with liquid — 55%

Source: ASH

Comparison with other surveys

In 2014, questions on electronic cigarette use were added to surveys carried out in schools by governments in Wales[56] Scotland[7] and England[89]. The patterns of electronic cigarette use among all these surveys and the ASH Smokefree GB Youth survey are similar. The surveys taken together indicate that regular

5. Moore, G., et al. *Electronic-cigarette use among young people in Wales: evidence from two cross-sectional surveys*. BMJ Open, 2015; Apr 15;5(4):e007072.

6. Moore, G.F., et al. *E-cigarette use and intentions to smoke among 10-11-year-old never-smokers in Wales*. Tob Control, 2014: pii. tobaccocontrol-2014-052011. [Epub ahead of print]

7. ISD Scotland. *Scottish School's Adolescent Lifestyle and Substance Use Survey (SALSUS)* 2014. 18 May 2015; Available from: http://www.isdscotland.org/Health-Topics/Public-Health/SALSUS/.

8. Hughes, K., et al. *Associations between e-cigarette access and smoking and drinking behaviours in teenagers*. BMC Public Health, 2015;15:244.

9. What About Youth? Study. Base = 117,577 15-year-olds in England for questions on e-cigarettes.

electronic cigarette use among young people is a relatively rare phenomenon and is largely among young people who smoke. The surveys do, however, show a higher level of 'experimentation' with electronic cigarettes (young people who have tried products one or twice). This too is much more common among children who smoke but can also be observed among children who have never smoked. Some differences between the surveys do exist – for example the high number of young people who had 'ever tried' electronic-cigarettes in the Smoking, Drinking and Use (SDD) Survey was very high. These can be explained by differing methodologies and differently worded questions. For example, SDD prompts young people to consider use as "even a puff or two" whereas the ASH Smokefree GB Youth survey does not include this prompt.

As awareness of and experimentation with electronic cigarettes grows it might be expected that we will see more young people regularly using the products. This will be an important area to watch particularly as age of sale restrictions come into force in England in October 2015.[9]

For further information about electronic cigarettes please see the ASH Website or download the ASH Briefing on *Electronic cigarettes* or the ASH Factsheet on *Use of Electronic Cigarettes Among Adults in Great Britain*.

October 2016

⇨ The above information is reprinted with kind permission from ASH. Please visit ash.org.uk for further information.

© 2017 ASH

E-cigarette use among young people

Source	Ever tried (%)	Use more than once a month but less than once a week (not just once or twice) (%)	Use more than once a week (%)	Use more than once a month in never smokers (%)	Regular smokers who had tried e-cigarettes (%)
ASH Smokefree GB youth survey (11–18 years) 2016, March	12.0	0.7	0.9	0.3	70
Health behaviour in school-aged children, Wales (11–16 years), Nov 2013–Feb 2014	12.3	1.5	0.3	Not reported	
CHETS Wales survey (10–11-year-olds) 2014	5.8	Not reported	Not reported	Not reported	Not reported
SALSUS Scotland survey (15- and 13-year-olds), 2015	23.6	1.5	2.3	0.5	90.1
The smoking, drinking and drug use survey (11–15-year-olds), 2014	22	3	1	Not reported	89
What about YOUth survey (15-year-olds), 2014	18	2	1	0	84

Social media is nothing like drugs, despite all the horror stories

THE CONVERSATION

***An article from* The Conversation.**

By Andy Przybylski, Associate Professor and Senior Research Fellow, University of Oxford and Amy C Orben, College Lecturer and DPhil Candidate, University of Oxford

Letting your child use social media is like giving them cocaine, alcohol and cigarettes – all at once, or so we're told. If you have been following recent press reports about the effects of social media on young people, you may well believe this. But there is no scientific evidence to support such extreme claims.

"Media reports that compare social media to drug use are ignoring evidence of positive effects, while exaggerating and generalising the evidence of negative effects"

The real story is far more complex. It is very difficult to predict how social media will affect any specific individual – the effect depends on things like their personality, type of social media use and social surroundings. In reality, social media can have both positive and negative outcomes.

For a claim to be proved scientifically it needs to be thoroughly tested. To fully confirm *The Independent's* headline that: "Giving your child a smartphone is like giving them a gram of cocaine, says top addiction expert", you would need to give children both a gram of cocaine and a smartphone and then compare the effects. Similarly, you would need to provide millennials with social media, drugs and alcohol to test *The Conversation's* headline that: "Social media is as harmful as alcohol and drugs for millennials". But ethical guidelines at universities were put in place so that such studies will never be done.

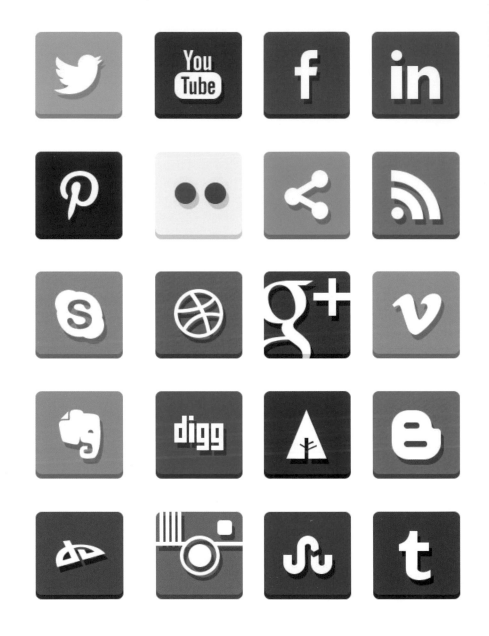

The diversity of social media

But maybe news headlines should be discounted – as exaggerations are often used to grab the readers' attention. But even when ignoring these grand claims, the media coverage of social media is still misleading. For example, reports that talk about the effects of social media are often oversimplifying reality. Social media is incredibly diverse – different sites providing a host of different features. This makes it extremely difficult to generalise about social media's effects.

Focusing on the negative

Past media coverage has not only oversimplified social media, but has often only focused on social media's negative aspects. But scientific research demonstrates that there are both positive and negative outcomes of social media use. Research has shown that Facebook increases self-esteem and promotes feeling connected to others. People's physiological reactions also indicate they react positively to Facebook use.

"A recent review of past research concluded that the effect of Facebook depends on which of the platform's features you use. A dialogue with friends over Facebook messenger can improve your mood, while comparing your life to other people's photos on the Newsfeed can do the opposite"

By contrast, it has also been found that social media can decrease well-being and increases social anxiety. An analysis of 57 scientific studies found that social media is associated with slightly higher levels of narcissism. This array of conflicting evidence suggests that social media has both negative and positive effects. Not just one or the other.

The amount matters

The effect of social media also depends on the amount of time you spend using it. In a recent study we conducted of more than 120,000 UK teenagers, we found that moderate social media use is not harmful to mental health.

"Those who use screens a moderate amount report higher well-being compared with those who didn't use social media at all and those who used it"

Recent media reports may have made parents unnecessarily anxious about their child's use of social media. A flashy quote or headline can often distract from the real challenges of parenting. It's time the media covered not only the bad, but also the beneficial and complex sides of social media. The effects of social media cannot be summarised by comparing social media to drugs. It is just not that simple.

18 June 2017

⇨ The above information is reprinted with kind permission from *The Conversation*. Please visit www.theconversation.com for further information.

© The Conversation Trust (UK)

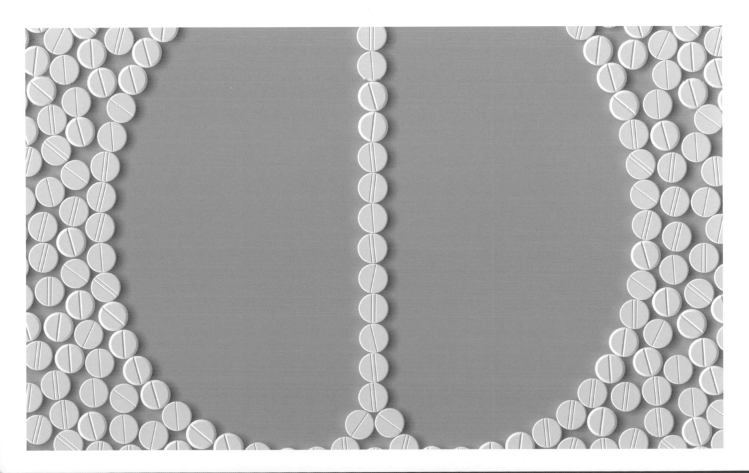

Children "becoming hunchbacks" due to addiction to smart phones

Chiropractor claims that young people who spend hours hunched over electronic devices are seriously damaging their necks and spines, as witnessed by the rise in cases of 'text neck'.

Children as young as seven are developing hunchbacks and curved spines because of the hours spent bending over smartphones and tablets, a chiropractor has claimed.

Dr James Carter warned that he had seen an "alarming increase" in the condition, which he called "text neck".

He said patients often came in complaining of a headache but that a simple heel-to-toe test revealed that they had developed a backwards curve in the neck having spent hours hunched over electronic devices.

"I have started seeing lots of cases over the past two years, especially in young schoolchildren and teenagers," Dr Carter told Daily Mail Australia.

"The condition is called 'text neck' because it is often caused when people sit with their heads dropped forward looking at their devices for several hours at a time.

"Instead of a normal forward curve, patients can be seen to have a backwards curve. It can be degenerative, often causing head, neck, shoulder and back pain.

"Many patients come in complaining they have a headache, but we actually find text neck is the cause of it. They often fail a simple heel-to-toe test and tend to fall over."

Are smartphones making our children mentally ill?

Sammy Margo, from the UK's Chartered Society of Physiotherapy, agreed that "text neck" was on the rise.

She said: "When you drop your chin on to your chest for a long period you are stretching the whole structure.

"Eventually, in conjunction with a sedentary lifestyle, it could lead to serious consequences."

Dr Carter, from Niagara Park on Australia's New South Wales Central Coast, warned that the condition could lead to anxiety and depression as well as spinal damage.

And he said 50 per cent of the patients he diagnosed were school-aged children and teenagers.

A recent survey by the consultancy ComRes for Channel 4 News found just over half of parents worried their kids were exposed to sexual content on their electronic devices, while 52 per cent said they were worried about them meeting strangers online.

It also found that children spend an average of nearly three hours a day in front of their screens – whether playing games, watching videos on YouTube or using social media.

Dr Carter advised avoiding using laptops or phones while sitting or lying in bed and raising monitors or devices to eye level.

Dr Chris McCarthy, a consultant spinal physiotherapist at Imperial College Healthcare NHS Trust in London, cautioned against the use of X-rays to diagnose such a condition.

He expressed concern that patients suspecting they had the condition would go to their GP and expect to have an X-ray, which he said were not recommended in the treatment of neck pain and would expose them to unnecessary radiation.

Whilst he said he had heard of "text neck", he suggested that the broader problem was more likely to stem from a sedentary lifestyle and a general lack of exercise.

"Non-specific neck pain can be related to sedentary postures," he said.

"As physios, we would support a notion that if a child does not do any exercise and stays in a static position playing computer games and on Facebook there is more chance they will get spinal pain, including in the neck."

17 July 2017

⇨ The above information is reprinted with kind permission from *The Telegraph*. Please visit www.telegraph.co.uk for further information.

Physical activity levels tail off in boys and girls from age seven

Physical activity levels may start tailing off as early as seven years old, rather than during adolescence as is widely believed, new research reveals.

The findings of a study by Newcastle University and the University of Strathclyde, published online in the *British Journal of Sports Medicine*, question the assumption that decline only happens among teens and is gender-specific.

And there is no evidence to indicate that the decline is greater among girls than it is among boys, the results show.

Researchers say the prevailing view among policy-makers and health professionals is that physical activity levels during childhood are adequate, but fall sharply during adolescence, and that the decline is significantly greater among girls.

But there is little hard evidence to back this up, and what research has been carried out in this area has mostly been done before the impact of new technologies would have been felt, the experts add.

Preventing decline of physical activity

Professor Ashley Adamson, of Newcastle University's Human Nutrition Research Centre, is a co-author of the paper.

She said: "Our study questions the concept of the adolescent girl as a priority for research and policy efforts in physical activity. Future research and public health policy should focus on preventing the decline in physical activity which begins in childhood, not adolescence, in both girls and boys.

"There needs to be an improved understanding of the determinants of the different physical activity patterns, including an understanding of the importance of biological and environmental influences."

In a bid to quantify the timing of any changes, experts tracked the physical activity levels of a representative sample of around 400 children taking part in the Gateshead Millennium Cohort Study from 2006 to 2015.

Physical activity levels were measured when the children were seven, nine, 12 and 15, using a small lightweight portable monitor, worn for seven days at a time.

The monitor – known as an actigraph – recorded activity for 15-second intervals, and was removed only at night, and for bathing/swimming.

As an additional back-up, the families involved were asked to log when the devices were worn and removed each day.

Overall, the total volume of physical activity fell from the age of seven onwards in both boys and girls during this time, with declines no steeper during adolescence than in earlier childhood. But the decline was not uniform, the data showed.

Activity levels of boys and girls

Four distinct patterns emerged for the boys: low levels that slowly tailed off from the age of seven (3%); initially high but rapidly declining

levels from the age of seven (17%); moderate levels that gradually tailed off from the age of seven (61%); and stable levels of moderate to vigorous physical activity throughout (19%).

There were three different patterns among the girls: low levels of physical activity to start with, which slowly declined from the age of seven (19%); moderate levels that gradually tailed off from the age of seven (62%); and high initial levels that fell sharply from the age of seven onwards (19%).

This is an observational study, so no firm conclusions can be drawn about cause and effect, added to which, although representative of North East England, the study findings may not be applicable to other areas of the country, or other nations, say the researchers.

But they point out: "The present study found that 100% of boys and girls fitted into longitudinal trajectories which were inconsistent with the orthodox view that physical activity begins to decline at adolescence, declines much more rapidly at adolescence and/or declines much more rapidly in adolescent girls than boys."

The research did not set out to examine the reasons behind the changes, but finding out why around one in five of the boys managed to maintain levels of moderate to vigorous physical activity throughout the study period might help to inform future policy and practice, they suggest.

But the findings indicate that a shift in research focus might be warranted, they say. "The study questions the concept of the adolescent girl as a priority for research and policy efforts in physical activity," they point out.

Reference

Timing of the decline in physical activity in childhood and adolescence: Gateshead Millennium Cohort Study. Mohammed Abdulaziz Farooq, Kathryn N Parkinson, Ashley J Adamson, Mark S Pearce, Jessica K Reilly, Adrienne R Hughes, Xanne Janssen, Laura Basterfield, John J Reilly. British Journal of Sports Medicine 2017 http://dx.doi.org/10.1136/ bjsports-2016-096933

14 March 2017

⇨ The above information is reprinted with kind permission from the BMJ. Please visit bmj. com for further information.

⇨ Citation: *Timing of the decline in physical activity in childhood and adolescence: Gateshead Millennium Cohort Study.* Mohammed Abdulaziz Farooq, Kathryn N Parkinson, Ashley J Adamson, Mark S Pearce, Jessica K Reilly, Adrienne R Hughes, Xanne Janssen, Laura Basterfield, John J Reilly. British *Journal of Sports Medicine* 2017 http://dx.doi.org/10.1136/ bjsports-2016-096933

Adolescents: health risks and solutions

Key facts

⇨ Estimated 1.2 million adolescents died in 2015, over 3,000 every day, mostly from preventable or treatable causes.

⇨ Road traffic injuries were the leading cause of death in 2015. Other major causes of adolescent deaths include lower respiratory infections, suicide, diarrhoeal diseases and drowning.

⇨ Globally, there are 44 births per 1,000 to girls aged 15 to 19 per year.

⇨ Half of all mental health disorders in adulthood start by age 14, but most cases are undetected and untreated.

Around 1.2 billion people, or one in six of the world's population, are adolescents aged ten to 19.

"Reducing the marketing of foods high in saturated fats, trans-fatty acids, free sugars, or salt and providing access to healthy foods and opportunities to engage in physical activity are important for all but especially children and adolescents"

Most are healthy, but there is still substantial premature death, illness, and injury among adolescents. Illnesses can hinder their ability to grow and develop to their full potential. Alcohol or tobacco use, lack of physical activity, unprotected sex and/or exposure to violence can jeopardise not only their current health, but also their health as adults, and even the health of their future children.

Promoting healthy behaviours during adolescence, and taking steps to better protect young people from health risks are critical for the prevention of health problems in adulthood, and for countries' future health and ability to develop and thrive.

Main health issues include: early pregnancy and childbirth

The leading cause of death for 15–19-year-old girls globally is complications from pregnancy and childbirth.

Some 11% of all births worldwide are to girls aged 15–19 years, and the vast majority of these births are in low- and middle-income countries. The UN Population Division puts the global adolescent birth rate in 2015 at 44 births per 1,000 girls this age – country rates range from 1 to over 200 births per 1,000 girls. This indicates a marked decrease since 1990. This decrease is reflected in a similar decline in maternal mortality rates among 15–19-year-olds.

One of the specific targets of the health Sustainable Development Goal (SDG 3) is that by 2030, the world should ensure universal access to sexual and reproductive healthcare services, including for family planning, information and education, and the integration of reproductive health into national strategies and programmes. To support this, a proposed indicator for the Global strategy for women's, children's and adolescents' health is the adolescent birth rate.

Better access to contraceptive information and services can reduce the number of girls becoming pregnant and giving birth at too young an age. Laws that specify a minimum age of marriage at 18 and which are enforced can help.

Girls who do become pregnant need access to quality antenatal care. Where permitted by law, adolescents who opt to terminate their pregnancies should have access to safe abortion.

HIV

More than two million adolescents are living with HIV. Although the overall number of HIV-related deaths is down 30% since the peak in 2006, estimates suggest that HIV deaths among adolescents are rising. This increase, which has been predominantly in the WHO African Region, may reflect the fact that although more children with HIV survive into adolescence, they do not all then get the care and support they need to remain in good health and prevent transmission. In sub-Saharan Africa only 10% of young men and 15% of young women aged 15 to 24 are aware of their HIV status.

One of the specific targets of the health Sustainable Development Goal (SDG 3) is that by 2030 there should be an end to the epidemics of AIDS, tuberculosis, malaria and neglected tropical diseases, hepatitis, water-borne diseases and other communicable diseases. Given the high prevalence of HIV in many countries, to achieve this, adolescents will need to be central to control efforts.

Young people need to know how to protect themselves and must have the means to do so. This includes being able to obtain condoms to prevent sexual transmission of the virus and clean needles and syringes for those who inject drugs. Better access to HIV testing and counselling, and stronger subsequent links to HIV treatment services for those who test HIV positive, are also needed.

Other infectious diseases

Thanks to improved childhood vaccination, adolescent deaths and disability from measles have fallen markedly – for example, by 90% in the African Region between 2000 and 2012. Diarrhoea and lower respiratory tract infections are estimated to be among the top five causes of death for ten to 19-year-olds. These two diseases, together with meningitis, are the top three causes of adolescent death in African low and middle-income countries (LMICs).

Mental health

Depression is the third leading cause of illness and disability among adolescents, and suicide is the third leading cause of death in older adolescents (15–19 years). Violence, poverty, humiliation and feeling devalued can increase the risk of developing mental health problems.

Building life skills in children and adolescents and providing them with psychosocial support in schools and other community settings can help promote good mental health. Programmes to help strengthen the ties between adolescents and their families are also important. If problems arise, they should be detected and managed by competent and caring health workers.

Violence

Violence is a leading cause of death in older adolescent males. Interpersonal violence represents 43% of all adolescent male deaths in LMICs in the WHO Americas Region. Globally, one in ten girls under the age of 20 years report experiencing sexual violence.

Promoting nurturing relationships between parents and children early in life, providing training in life skills, and reducing access to alcohol and firearms can help to prevent injuries and deaths due to violence. Effective and empathetic care for adolescent survivors of violence and ongoing support can help deal with the physical and psychological consequences.

Alcohol and drugs

Harmful drinking among adolescents is a major concern in many countries. It reduces self-control and increases risky behaviours, such as unsafe sex or dangerous driving. It is a primary cause of injuries (including those due to road traffic accidents), violence (especially by a partner) and premature deaths. It can also lead to health problems in later life and affect life expectancy. Setting a minimum age for buying and consuming alcohol and regulating how alcoholic drinks are targeted at the younger market are among the strategies for reducing harmful drinking.

Drug use among 15–19-year-olds is also an important global concern. Drug control may focus on reducing drug demand, drug supply, or both, and successful programmes usually include structural, community and individual-level interventions.

Injuries

Unintentional injuries are the leading cause of death and disability among adolescents. In 2015, over 115,000 adolescents died as a result of road traffic accidents. Young drivers need advice on driving safely, while laws that prohibit driving under the influence of alcohol and drugs need to be strictly enforced. Blood alcohol levels need to be set lower for teenage drivers. Graduated licences for novice drivers with zero-tolerance for drink-driving are recommended.

Drowning is also a major cause of death among adolescents – 57,000 adolescents, two-thirds of them boys, are estimated to have drowned in 2015, and teaching children and adolescents to swim is an essential intervention to prevent these deaths.

"Developing healthy eating and exercise habits in adolescence are foundations for good health in adulthood"

Malnutrition and obesity

Many boys and girls in developing countries enter adolescence undernourished, making them more vulnerable to disease and early death. At the other end of the spectrum, the number of adolescents who are overweight or obese is increasing in low, middle and high-income countries.

Exercise and nutrition

Iron deficiency anaemia is the leading cause of years lost to death and disability in 2015. Iron and folic acid supplements are a solution that also helps to promote health before adolescents become parents. Regular deworming in areas where intestinal helminths such as hookworm are common is recommended to prevent micronutrient (including iron) deficiencies.

Tobacco use

The vast majority of people using tobacco today began doing so when they were adolescents. Prohibiting the sale of tobacco products to minors and increasing the price of tobacco products through higher taxes, banning tobacco advertising and ensuring smoke-free environments are crucial. Globally, at least one in ten adolescents aged 13 to 15 years uses tobacco, although there are areas where this figure is much higher. Cigarette smoking seems to be decreasing among younger adolescents in some high-income countries.

Rights of adolescents

The rights of children (people under 18 years of age) to survive, grow and develop are enshrined in international legal documents. In 2013, the Committee on the Rights of the Child (CRC), which oversees the child rights convention, published guidelines on the right of children and adolescents to the enjoyment of the highest attainable standard of health, and a General Comment on realising the rights of children during adolescence was published in 2016. It highlights states' obligations to recognise the special health and development needs and rights of adolescents and young people.

The Convention on the Elimination of Discrimination Against Women (CEDAW) also sets out the rights of women and girls to health and adequate health care.

May 2017

⇨ The above information is reprinted with kind permission from the World Health Organization. Please visit www.who.int for further information.

Why sugar is so much worse for teenagers' brains

An article from The Conversation.

By Amy Reichelt, Lecturer, ARC DECRA, RMIT University

THE CONVERSATION

The rate of obesity is increasing worldwide and the increase has been particularly dramatic in young people. Young people are the greatest consumers of high-energy, sugary and fat-laden "junk" foods and sweetened drinks.

The heightened metabolism and rapid growth during puberty can protect against obesity. However, easy access to cheap junk foods and increasingly sedentary lifestyles outweighs the protection from growth spurts.

Diets high in refined sugar and saturated fat not only contribute to weight gain and associated health issues, but also have a profoundly detrimental impact on brain function.

It is known excessive consumption of junk foods damage areas of the brain essential for learning and memory processes. Neurons in brain regions, including the hippocampus, that encodes memories, no longer work efficiently, leading to poorer learning.

This is of great concern as adolescence is a critical formative period for learning about the world. Adolescence is also a time of newly found independence, including food choices.

Recent research in rodents has shown the adolescent brain is at an increased risk of developing diet-induced cognitive dysfunction. Adolescent, but not adult, mice develop memory problems after consuming high-fat diets.

Teenage rats that drank sugary beverages were less able to remember a specific location leading to an escape hatch. This was compared to adult rats drinking sugary beverages, and teenage rats that had low-sugar diets.

The brains of the adolescent sugar-diet rats also showed increased levels of inflammation in the hippocampus, disrupting learning and memory function. Inflammation in the brain can contribute to cognitive decline and dementia.

The negative effects of obesity on the brain have been observed in young people too. Obese adolescents performed worse at maths, spelling and mental flexibility than healthy-weight adolescents. Structural brain scans revealed that obese teenagers had smaller hippocampi. This provides evidence that excessive body fat impacts the brain's learning centre.

Teenage brains are a work in progress

The teenage brain undergoes major developmental changes in terms of structure and function. Adolescence is a period of increased neuroplasticity due to the dramatic changes in connectivity within brain regions.

Brain-imaging studies show that the prefrontal cortex doesn't fully mature until the early 20s. A major role of the prefrontal cortex is performing executive functions. This term encapsulates behavioural control, attention and decision-making.

Poor regulation of the prefrontal cortex during adolescence can explain the increased risk-taking behaviours in teenagers, including dangerous driving, drug use and binge drinking.

Educational efforts to provide teens with information about unsafe behaviours tends to fall on deaf ears. The prefrontal cortex helps us to resist performing behaviours triggered by events in the environment. Resisting these behaviours in the face of immediate reward can be difficult, particularly for teenagers.

Teenage brains love rewards

The risky behaviours teenagers engage in are often immediately rewarding. The brain's reward system releases the neurotransmitter dopamine when stimulated by pleasurable events, increasing the drive to carry out these activities.

Teenagers are particularly drawn to rewards, including eating tasty foods high in fat and sugar. The adolescent reward system is sensitive to stimulation and may be permanently altered by overactivation during this period.

Combined with the reduced ability to resist rewarding behaviours, it is not surprising that teenagers prefer to eat foods that are easy to obtain and immediately gratifying, even in the face of health advice to the contrary.

Changes in the brain caused by overconsumption of sugary foods during adolescence can manifest in later life as difficulties in experiencing reward. Research has shown male rats that drank sugar water during adolescence showed reduced motivation and enjoyment of rewards when they were adults.

These behaviours are core features of mood disorders including depression. Importantly, this shows that how we eat during adolescence can impact brain function as adults, leading to long-lasting changes in food preference and learning about rewards.

Teenage brains are more plastic

Excessive consumption of junk foods during adolescence could derail normal brain maturation processes. This may alter normal development trajectories, leading to enduring behavioural predispositions – in this case, the habit of consuming fatty and sugar foods, leading to obesity.

Fortunately, the increased plasticity of the adolescent brain means that young people may be more responsive to change. Opportunities to identify and intervene in high-risk youths may avert destructive negative behavioural spirals that may originate in adolescence. This can encourage life-long healthy habits.

25 October 2016

⇨ The above information is reprinted with kind permission from *The Conversation*. Please visit theconversation.com for further information.

Why is diabetes killing so many teenagers?
THE CONVERSATION

An article from The Conversation.

By Kathleen Gillespie, Reader in Molecular Medicine, University of Bristol

Young British men have a problem with diabetes. Recent studies have highlighted that death rates from type 1 diabetes in boys and men aged 15 to 24 years have almost doubled since 2000 in the UK. This is higher than reported death rates among young men with diabetes in other European countries. Why has type 1 diabetes become such a problem for our young people?

Overall, about 10% of people with diabetes have type 1 diabetes. The condition is caused when the immune system makes a mistake. The cells in the pancreas that make insulin are crucial for controlling blood glucose levels, but in a patient with type 1 diabetes the immune system treats these cells as a threat and targets them for destruction.

When about 70% of these "beta cells" have been destroyed there is no longer enough insulin to control blood sugars, which means the patient will need daily insulin injections. The condition is more common in children and young people with an average age at onset of 12 years.

Young people dying as a result of type 1 diabetes is rare but is possible if the condition is not diagnosed quickly. The disease is associated with increased risk of health complications, with particularly detrimental effects on the kidneys and eyes if the condition is not well managed. And poor management of insulin treatment can lead to blood glucose levels getting too high or too low, which can also cause death.

Type 1 diabetes is a growing problem in most developed countries, with particular increases among young people. From our research, as well as other studies, we know that the incidence of type 1 diabetes is increasing at a rate of 3% per year in most European populations. The rate is even higher in children diagnosed under the age of five years.

The cause for this increase in the number of people diagnosed with type 1 diabetes is unclear. Certain genes occur more often in people with the disease but these genes are not becoming more frequent. Instead, it appears that some factors in our environment are increasing the risk of type 1 diabetes.

A lot of research is ongoing trying to determine what these factors are and how they contribute to the increasing numbers of people with the condition. In particular, a study called The Environmental Determinants of Diabetes in the Young (TEDDY) is examining early-life events including diet changes and viral infections.

But the increasing rates of type 1 diabetes cannot explain the rising death rate among young British men, because we know incidence of the disease is growing at similar rates in other European populations – but the diabetes-related deaths aren't rising at the same rate.

Poor management of diabetes can result from a combination of factors including changes during puberty, the lack of engagement by teenage boys with the healthcare system, and other social factors during a time in their lives when they may start living away from home. During this same period, young men in the UK also transition from childhood to adult NHS services and this could result in loss of follow-up for some patients.

National data showing increased rates of diabetes-related complications in teenagers supports the view that there is an urgent need to focus on this age group. We need to ensure that all young people with diabetes attend all clinic appointments and that there is a support mechanism in place for those who have difficulties coping with their condition.

Perhaps research studies could be designed to establish whether social networks could be used to help young people who manage their diabetes well to help those who have problems.

Ultimately, if successful, this could save lives and save the NHS money by helping to prevent conditions such as diabetic kidney disease.

30 April 2015

⇨ The above information is reprinted with kind permission from *The Conversation*. Please visit www.theconversation.com/why-is-diabetes-killing-so-many-teenagers-40981 for further information.

One in three older teenagers have been too stressed to sleep

More than a third of 16- and 17-year-olds are so anxious that they have suffered sleepless nights in the last year, according to new research from The Children's Society.

Seriously Awkward, launched today, reveals that we are in danger of creating a "worried generation" of 16- and 17-year-olds, with one in three (34%) saying they frequently feel anxious and a quarter (25%) reporting they often feel sad. One in four say they do not feel optimistic about the future.

The report, based on an Opinium poll of over 1,000 16- and 17-year-olds across the UK, and new analysis, shows two in three (69%) said they felt judged simply for being a teenager.

"More than a third of 16- and 17-year-olds are so anxious that they have suffered sleepless nights in the last year, according to new research from The Children's Society"

And the concern is mirrored among parents. Seven in ten (70%) parents agree that life is tougher for teenagers now than it was for them.

The Children's Society's new Seriously Awkward campaign highlights the huge challenges that 16- and 17-year-olds face. They are more likely to go missing or be a victim of violent crime than any other age group and they are at a high risk of sexual exploitation and domestic violence.

Yet they are being systematically let down by the law and don't get the same basic safeguards as younger children. For instance, while laws exist to protect 16- and 17-year-olds against specific incidents such as assault or sexual offences, there is no catch-all law to protect them from sustained child cruelty and neglect in the same way as there is for younger children.

The charity is lobbying for a change in the law to protect children aged 16 and 17 from abuse and neglect, and to ensure that support services, such as Child and Adolescent Mental Health services, always treat them as children and offer them support when they need it.

An estimated half a million 16- and 17-year-olds face particular risk of harm because they are already dealing with multiple issues such as poverty, poor health or a lack of supportive relationships.

Beatrice Morris, 17, a student from London says: "I've had anxiety and depression throughout my teens. At my lowest ebb, I was surviving on two hours sleep at night and was self-harming. It took years for me to get the mental health support I needed.

"Teenagers are under so much pressure. We're constantly being told by society that we are lazy or up to no good and at the same time we're also expected to do well and get a job or go to university.

"But the odds are stacked against us. The cost of going to university has rocketed up, salaries are low and most people my age aren't hopeful about the future. At 16 and 17 we're expected to be resilient and behave like adults but we don't have the same rights as adults and can't make our voices heard."

At the time when these teenagers need the most help, support for things such as mental health or housing is woefully inadequate and they often fall through the gaps between children's and adult services. The lack of provision for teenagers with mental health problems means many are placed on adult mental health wards or, in some cases, have even been detained in police cells.

And almost half (45%) of 16 and 17–year-olds asking their council for help with homelessness are turned away without being assessed for support.

Matthew Reed, Chief Executive of The Children's Society, says: "This research reveals that a generation of teenagers are being let down by society. Many are struggling with a range of issues but are dismissed as resilient enough to cope, and denied the same legal protection and services as younger children.

"Teenagers are under so much pressure. We're constantly being told by society that we are lazy or up to no good and at the same time we're also expected to do well and get a job or go to university"

There is a misconception that teenagers do not require as much protection as younger children. But they are so often more in need of help than any other age group. They have greater freedom than younger children which can put them in potentially risky situations such as being exposed to drugs, alcohol or adults who intend them harm.

Teenagers suffering abuse and neglect may be overlooked by children's services because they are deemed older and more resilient but lack financial independence to remove themselves from harmful situations.

13 July 2015

⇨ The above information is reprinted with kind permission from The Children's Society. Please visit www.childrenssociety.org.uk for further information.

© 2017 The Children's Society

Protecting teenagers in the UK against meningitis

It's really important for teenagers to be protected from meningitis and septicaemia. Although babies and young children are most vulnerable to these diseases, teenagers and students are the next most at-risk group.

Meningitis and septicaemia are deadly diseases that can strike without warning, killing one in ten of those affected, and leaving a third of survivors with life-altering after-effects that can be as severe as deafness, brain damage and loss of limbs.

⇨ Meningitis is the inflammation of the lining around the brain and spinal cord

⇨ Septicaemia is the blood poisoning form of the disease

The most common cause of life-threatening meningitis and septicaemia in the UK is meningococcal infection. Teenagers and young adults are the age group that are most likely to carry meningococcal bacteria in their nose and throat, partly because they mix with so many other young people, some of whom are unknowingly carrying the meningitis bacteria.

The vast majority of people who carry the bacteria do not become unwell or develop any symptoms but when they unknowingly pass the bacteria on to someone who is susceptible, meningitis or septicaemia may rapidly develop.

There are 12 different types of meningococcal meningitis and septicaemia. In the UK there are now vaccines available as part of the immunisation schedule to protect against the five most common types (Men A, B, C, W and Y).

Teenagers are routinely offered vaccination in school with the MenACWY vaccine – which protects against Men A, C, W and Y. The charity Meningitis Research Foundation (MRF) encourages all teenagers who are offered the vaccine, whether through their GP surgery or at school, to make sure they get vaccinated.

This vaccine programme was bought in especially to deal with a rise in deadly MenW disease which was mainly affecting teenagers. Not only does the vaccine directly protect teenagers, it will also protect others who haven't been vaccinated, because there is very good research evidence that vaccinating people with the MenACWY vaccine stops them from 'carrying' the bacteria at the back of the nose and throat and passing it on to other people.

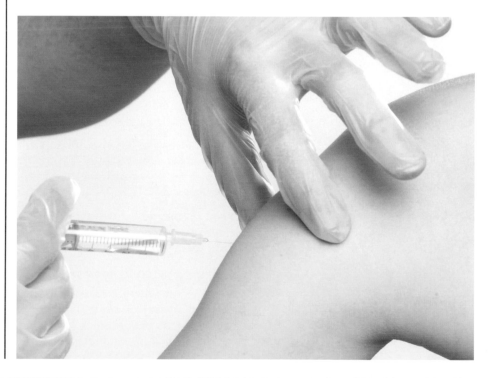

A different vaccine – the MenB vaccine – is available but only babies are routinely vaccinated against MenB. The MenB vaccine is not offered to older children or to teenagers.

MenB is the most common cause of life-threatening meningitis and septicaemia in the UK. MRF wants to see teenagers protected against MenB and is currently funding research to find out whether vaccinating teenagers against MenB can stop them from carrying the bacteria so they cannot pass it on to others.

Until there are effective vaccines to prevent all types of meningitis and septicaemia, teenagers should be aware of the symptoms of the disease.

The symptoms in teenagers can include:

⇨ Fever and/or vomiting

⇨ Severe headache

⇨ Limb, joint, muscle pain

⇨ Cold hands and feet, shivering

⇨ Pale

⇨ Breathing fast, breathless

⇨ Rash

⇨ Stiff neck

⇨ Dislike of bright lights

⇨ Very sleepy, difficult to wake, vacant

⇨ Confused, delirious

⇨ Seizures (fits).

Recognising the disease early and getting medical help quickly provides the best chances of a good recovery from the disease.

2017

⇨ The above information is reprinted with kind permission from the Meningitis Research Foundation. For more information visit www. meningitis.org or call the free helpline 080 8800 3344.

© Meningitis Research Foundation 2017

Are you ready for sex?
Find out the things you need to ask yourself if you're thinking about having sex.

Most people have sex for the first time when they're 16 or older, not before. If someone's boasting about having sex, it's possible they're pretending.

There are no rules about how long you have to be going out with someone before you have sex. Being ready happens at different times for everyone – don't decide to have sex just because your friends or partner are pressuring you.

You can read this whole article or go straight to the sections to find out more:

⇨ Sex and the law

⇨ Deciding when to have sex

⇨ How to talk about sex

⇨ The questions to ask yourself about sex

⇨ How do I bring up the subject of safer sex?

⇨ Lesbian, gay or bisexual sex

⇨ Reading the signs they want sex

⇨ Alcohol won't help.

Sex and the law

The law says it's legal for you to agree – or consent – to sex from the age of 16.

If you're under 16, you can get confidential contraceptive and sexual health services, including advice about an unplanned pregnancy.

You can get free condoms from some GPs, community contraceptive or young persons' clinics, and Brook services.

If you're under 13, the situation is different because the law says you can't consent to any sexual activity at this age.

Read *Will they tell my parents?* to find out more about confidentiality, whatever your age.

Deciding when to have sex

Working out when you're ready to have sex and feeling comfortable about it is one of life's big decisions. You're the only one who can, and should, decide.

Just because you've had sex before, even with the same person, doesn't mean you have to do it again.

How to talk about sex

It's better to have an embarrassing talk about sex than an embarrassing sexual experience before you're ready.

There are lots of things to think and talk about, such as:

⇨ Are you both ready?

⇨ Will you be having sex for the right reasons, and not because of peer pressure or partner pressure?

⇨ Do you have contraception sorted?

Sex isn't the only aspect of a relationship, and there are other ways of enjoying each other's company. Discuss what you want and what you don't want to do.

You can do other things you both like, such as talking, meeting each other's family and friends, going to gigs or the cinema, taking part in sport, walking, and listening to music.

The questions to ask yourself about sex

You need to have the confidence to work out how you want to respond if sex comes up and how far to go. Ask yourself if you feel comfortable.

Is it the right time, in the right place, and with the right person? Do you really trust the person, and do you feel the same way about one another?

If you think you might have sex, ask yourself the following questions:

⇨ Does it feel right?

⇨ Do I love my partner?

- ⇨ Does he/she love me just as much?
- ⇨ Have we talked about using condoms to prevent STIs and HIV, and was the talk OK?
- ⇨ Have we got contraception organised to protect against pregnancy?
- ⇨ Do I feel able to say "no" at any point if I change my mind, and will we both be OK with that?

If you answer yes to all these questions, the time may be right. But if you answer yes to any of the following questions, it might not be:

- ⇨ Do I feel under pressure from anyone, such as my partner or friends?
- ⇨ Could I have any regrets afterwards?
- ⇨ Am I thinking about having sex just to impress my friends or keep up with them?
- ⇨ Am I thinking about having sex just to keep my partner?

Being in a relationship doesn't mean you have to have sex. Even if you've done it once or twice, you still need to make sure your boyfriend or girlfriend is as keen as you are each time.

How do I bring up the subject of safer sex?

When you decide to have sex, there's the possibility of pregnancy, catching a sexually transmitted infection (STI) such as chlamydia, or both. Whoever you're thinking of having sex with, it's important to talk about contraception and condoms before you have sex. Both of you have a responsibility to have this conversation.

Starting a conversation about the different types of contraception could be a good way to start talking about other issues to do with sex, such as how you feel about it and what you do and don't want to do.

You could try saying, "I found out there are 15 different types of contraception… If we were to have sex, which one should we use?"

Researching the options together will help both of you feel more confident and in control of the situation. Find out about the 15 different kinds of contraception.

You can get free and confidential advice about sex, contraception and abortion at any time. Visit your local doctor, community contraceptive clinic, sexual health or genitourinary medicine (GUM) clinic, or young persons' clinic. Call the national sexual health helpline on 0300 123 7123 for details. Find your local sexual health services.

Using condoms

You need to use condoms to reduce the risk of catching an STI, including HIV, whoever you're having sex with.

If you're in a boy/girl couple, you should use an additional form of contraception to prevent an unintended pregnancy.

Choosing the right contraception

There are 15 different kinds of contraception, including the implant, the injection, the combined pill, and the progestogen-only pill.

Most kinds of contraception are used by girls, but both of you have a responsibility to talk about this: a pregnancy will affect both of you.

Lesbian, gay or bisexual sex

If you have lesbian, gay or bisexual sex, it's important to use a condom every time as you can still get or pass on STIs, including HIV. You also need to know about contraception in case you have straight sex as well.

Find out more about sexual health for women who have sex with women and men who have sex with men.

Reading the signs they want sex

Many people are surprised when a situation leads to sex, so learn to read the signs. If someone suggests you find a quiet place, makes lots of physical contact, or suddenly tries to charm and flatter you, they might be thinking about sex, even if you're not.

You need to decide whether you want to have sex. Don't let someone else decide for you by just going along with it. Make the decision in advance and stay in control of the situation – especially if you've had alcohol, because you'll be less inhibited.

If you're not sure you can stay in control, avoid situations that could lead to sex, such as going to someone's room or somewhere quiet.

Alcohol won't help

Many people have sex or lose their virginity when they've been drinking. After a few drinks, you're more likely to lose your judgement, and may do things you wouldn't do normally. You may regret your actions in the morning, and you won't be able to undo what you've done.

People are also more likely to have sex without a condom when they're drunk. This can lead to an STI or unintended pregnancy.

19 July 2017

- ⇨ The above information is reprinted with kind permission from NHS Choices. Please visit www.nhs.uk for further information.

© 2017 NHS Choices

Key facts

- 70% of young people who experience a mental health problem do not receive the appropriate support. (page 1)

- One in ten children and young people are affected by a mental health problem. (page 1)

- In the 2014/15 Child Line review, the results for the top ten reasons why young people contact Child Line show their main areas of concern. The top concern for young people was family relationships, including conflict in the family and parents' divorce or separation. Over 12 months, there were over 38,000 counselling sessions for this concern. (page 1)

- The Young Minds charity reported that, in 2008, 72% of children living in care were experiencing behavioural or emotional problems. These children were regarded as some of the most vulnerable people in UK society. (page 2)

- There is no single cause to an eating disorder, but it is estimated that almost 1.6 million people in the UK are affected. (page 2)

- ONS research into children's mental health and well-being found that one in eight children aged ten to 15 reported symptoms of mental ill-health in 2011 to 2012. (page 5)

- Research, funded by Macquarie, based on a survey of 2,215 respondents aged 16 to 25, found that the vast majority of young people (78%) think there is a stigma attached to mental health issues. (page 6)

- A third (32%) of those young people who would keep quiet about their mental health worries think admitting to a problem could affect their job prospects, 57% wouldn't want anyone to know they were struggling and 35% fear it would make them "look weak". (page 6)

- A recent study showed that 27% of [children and young people] who died had experienced exam stress or other academic pressures, but we don't know what proportion of under-20s in the general population also experience exam stress. However, one striking fact is that in 54% of cases there was a previous history of self-harm. And one in four had talked about suicide in the week before they died. (page 10)

- by the time young people reach the age of 17, nearly half (45%) claim they are "not confident". The pressures of exams, relationships and defining their identity can have an impact on confidence. At the age of 17, some teenagers also experience increasing levels of self-doubt as they are exposed to a constant tension between wanting to be the same as their friends (49%) and wanting to stand out as an individual (44%). (page 11)

- In a 2015 survey, over half of the respondents (54% range: 34% to 84%) reported that they had never smoked, while less than a quarter (21% range: 6% to 37%) reported they were "current smokers" (last 30 days). The proportion of students who started daily smoking at an early age (before 13) decreased over the 20 years: from 10% to 4%. Daily smoking, including early onset of this practice, continues to be more prevalent among boys, but the gender gap has narrowed over the 20 years as it has for smoking overall. Despite strict regulations on tobacco in most countries, over 60% of adolescents still reported relatively easy access to it. (page 15)

- In 2016, just under 21% of people surveyed in England, Scotland and Wales said they did not drink alcohol, equivalent to around 10.6 million adults aged 16 or over. That's two percentage points higher than in 2005, when the ONS first collected data on alcohol consumption. (page 25)

- Understanding of electronic cigarettes among children is generally good. Two-thirds of children who have heard of electronic cigarettes believe correctly that they are less harmful than cigarettes to the user (67%) although this has fallen over time, with increasing numbers of children believing they are equally harmful. (page 26)

- An estimated 1.2 million adolescents died in 2015, over 3,000 every day, mostly from preventable or treatable causes. (page 32)

- Road traffic injuries were the leading cause of death in 2015. Other major causes of adolescent deaths include lower respiratory infections, suicide, diarrhoeal diseases and drowning. (page 32)

- Globally, there are 44 births per 1,000 to girls aged 15 to 19 per year. (page 32)

- Half of all mental health disorders in adulthood start by age 14, but most cases are undetected and untreated. (page 32)

- Thanks to improved childhood vaccination, adolescent deaths and disability from measles have fallen markedly – for example, by 90% in the African Region between 2000 and 2012. (page 33)

- One in three (34%) 17-year-olds say they frequently feel anxious and a quarter (25%) report they often feel sad. One in four say they do not feel optimistic about the future. (page 36)

Glossary

Adolescent

A young person – someone in a transitional phase between child and adult.

Anxiety

Feeling nervous, worried or distressed, sometimes to a point where the person feels so overwhelmed that they find everyday life very difficult to handle.

Binge drinking

When an individual consumes large quantities of alcohol in one session, usually with the intention of becoming drunk, this is popularly referred to as 'binge drinking'. It is widely accepted that drinking four or more drinks in a short space of time constitutes 'bingeing', and this can have severe negative effects on people's health.

Cardiovascular disease

Conditions that affect the heart and circulation.

Cognitive enhancer

A substance that improves mental functions such as memory, recall and concentration.

Depression

Someone is said to be significantly depressed, or suffering from depression, when feelings of sadness or misery don't go away quickly and are so bad that they interfere with everyday life. Symptoms can also include low self-esteem and a lack of motivation. Depression can be triggered by a traumatic/difficult event (reactive depression), but not always (e.g. endogenous depression).

Exam stress

A feeling of nervousness, fear or worry before or during a test.

Legal high

Also known as psychoactive substances, legal highs function as stimulants and have mood-altering properties. Producing or trading in these substances will become illegal in the UK in 2016.

Long-term condition

A medical condition that cannot be cured but can be eased or controlled with medication.

Mental health

Sometimes called 'psychological well-being' or 'emotional health', mental health refers to the state of your mind and how a person can cope with everyday life. It is just as important as good physical health.

Methodology

The methods or systems used to undertake research or an area of study.

Nutritional standards

A set of regulations set by the Government to ensure that the food served in schools provides a healthy, balanced diet for children.

Psychoactive drug

A drug that affects the brain function, often resulting in changes of mood, behaviour or perception-levels.

Recreational drug

A drug that is taken occasionally and is often claimed to be non-addictive.

Risky behaviour

Behaviour that has the potential to get out of control or become dangerous.

Self-harm/self-injury

Self-harm is the act of deliberately injuring or mutilating oneself. People injure themselves in many different ways, including cutting, burning, poisoning or hitting parts of their body. Self-harmers often see harming as a coping strategy and give a variety of motivations for hurting themselves, including relieving stress or anxiety, focusing emotional pain and as a way of feeling in control. Although prevalent in young people, self-harm is found amongst patients of all ages. It is not usually an attempt to commit suicide, although people who self-harm are statistically more likely to take their own lives than those who don't.

Social media

Media which are designed specifically for electronic communication. 'Social networking' websites allow users to interact using instant messaging, share information, photos and videos and ultimately create an online community. Examples include Facebook, LinkedIn and micro-blogging site Twitter.

Stereotype

A fixed idea of a certain type of person or thing.

Assignments

Brainstorming

Brainstorm what you know about teenage health issues:

⇨ What kind of things count as 'risky behaviours'?

⇨ What are some of the mental health issues teenagers deal with?

Research

⇨ Research diabetes amongst young people. What causes diabetes? What are the treatments available? How can this condition be managed? Write a two page report on your findings.

⇨ Research the levels of physical activity in young people of your age group. How much exercise should they do in a week? Create an exercise plan which could fit into their daily routine. For example, use the stairs instead of a lift, walk instead of taking the bus.

⇨ Talk to some friends and family about their use of Social Media. Think of at least six questions to ask them and make a note of the respondents' age and gender. When you have gathered your information, write a summary of your findings. Include a graph showing the different types of Social Media used by different age groups and genders.

⇨ Did you know that sugar is bad for teenagers' brains? Research foods that have a high sugar content and make a graph to show your findings. Pick at least five different foods.

Design

⇨ Design a leaflet about mental health in teenagers. It should list the signs of depression and give ideas as to how to deal with this condition.

⇨ Read the article *Report highlights loneliness and lack of social integration amongst young people* on page 14. Design a poster highlighting the problem.

⇨ Choose an article from this book and design an illustration that highlights its key message.

⇨ Make an infographic from the table *Percentage of regular smokers aged 11–15 by sex: 1982–2014, England* shown on page 17.

⇨ Design an app that will give students tips and advise on how to cope with exam stress.

Oral

⇨ In small groups discuss the use of alcohol and drugs by young people. Write a list of reasons you think people use these substances. Share your findings with the rest of the class.

⇨ As a class discuss the pressures on young people to have sex. What does the law say? Discuss how alcohol can play a part in people making decisions they might later regret.

⇨ In pairs, one of you should play the role of a smoker and the other one should try to persuade them to give up. Then reverse the roles.

⇨ *Young adults in the UK are more likely to be teetotallers than their older counterparts, according to figures released this week.* Discuss this statement in small groups and feed back to the rest of the class.

⇨ Choose an illustration from this book and, in pairs, discuss what you think the artist was trying to portray with this image. Does the illustration work well with its accompanying article? If not, why not? How would you change it?

⇨ Interview your parents, teachers or others who are older than you and find out how healthy they were when they were younger. How much exercise did they do? What were their diets like? Do they feel healthier now? Write some notes and feedback to your class.

Reading/Writing

⇨ Write a definition of depression.

⇨ Write a two-page article on the use of social media and its affects on people.

⇨ Read the article *Iceland knows how to stop teen substance abuse but the rest of the world isn't listening* on page 19. Write a letter to your local council suggesting that if we provided more facilities for young people we might be able to reduce the levels of substance abuse by some people.

⇨ Imagine you are an Agony Aunt/Uncle and you have received a letter from a young boy telling you he is stressed about his forthcoming exams. He is frightened of letting his parents down as they have high expectations of him. He feels like he cannot cope and is feeling suicidal. Write a suitable reply.

⇨ Write a blog post imagining you are a teenager who is struggling to sleep.

⇨ Write an article about meningitis to highlight awareness in teenagers. What are the different types of meningitis? What symptoms should people be aware of and what treatments are available?

⇨ Write an article on the reluctance of young people to discuss their mental health issues. You should research whether boys or girls are more likely to talk about their feelings and supply evidence to support your conclusions.

addictions 15, 16
    drugs 20
    gambling 16
    gaming 16
    Internet Addiction Disorder 16
    and natural highs 20
    nicotine 18
ADHD 2
alcohol 15, 19, 22
    binge drinking 15, 25
    drink-driving 33
    impacts 33, 39
    substance abuse programmes 20
    and teetotalism 25
    treatment 24
anxiety 2, 36
    sleep problems 36

binge drinking 15, 25
boys and young men
    and addiction 16
    and diabetes 35, 36
    and exercise 31
    and mental health 11–12
    and suicide 8–9
brain 34
    and addiction 20
    and impairment 34
    and sugar 34–5

cannabis 15–16
contraception 39
crime 20

death and mortality 35
    leading causes of 32, 33
depression 2
diabetes 35–6
    and death 35
    impacts 35
    and insulin 35
drink-driving 33
drugs 15, 19–20, 21, 33 *see also individual drugs*
    addiction 20
    and social networking 28
    substance abuse programmes 20–1, 22–3
        risks 21–2
    treatment 24

e-cigarettes 17, 26, 27
    flavours 26
    and knowledge 26
eating disorders 2
employment 6
exams 10
exercise and activity 31–2, 33

football 22

girls and young women
    and addiction 16
    and exercise 31
    and mental health 11–12
    and suicide 8–9

health 32
    chronic conditions 13
    and smoking 17
HIV
    and death 32
    and knowledge 32–3

Iceland
    and alcohol 19, 20
    and drugs 19, 20–1, 23
    and smoking 20
    substance abuse programmes 19, 21, 22, 23
insulin 35
Internet Addiction Disorder 16

legal highs 16
Lithuania 22

meningitis 37, 38
    vaccination 37–8
mental health 1, 5, 6, 33
    and confidence levels 11–12
        and social networking 11
    and employment 6
    help and counselling 3, 4, 6–7, 36
        and funding 4
    risks 1–2
    social intelligence 14
    and social networking 5, 14
    and stigma 6
mental health services 8, 13
    waiting times 5
mental illness 1, 5, 8
mobile phones 30

neck pain 30
nicotine 18
nutrition 33

online gambling 16
online gaming 16
overweight and obesity 34

panic attacks 2
parents
    and drugs 20–1
    and mental health 1, 12
    and smoking 17
    and substance abuse programmes 21, 22
passive smoking 16
    in cars carrying children 18
    impacts 17
phobias 2

schools
    and mental health 4
    and smoking 17
SDGs 32–3

self-harm 2
    and suicide 10
septicaemia 37
sexual health 38–9
    and alcohol 39
    talking about 38, 39
    time factors 38
sexual orientation 39
sleep 36
smoking 15, 16, 17–19, 34
    addiction 18
    banning 18
    e-cigarettes 17, 26–7
    impacts 17
    passive smoking 16, 17, 18
    and prices 18
    substance abuse programmes 20
social intelligence 14
social isolation and loneliness 14
social networking 28–9
    and drugs 28
    and mental health 5, 11, 14
    time factors 29
sport and leisure activities 19, 21
    football 22
stress 10
sugar 34
    effects on the brain 34–5
suicide and suicidal thoughts 2–3, 7–9, 10
    definitions 8

teenage births 32
teenage pregnancy 32
teetotalism 25
text neck 30

violence 33

young people
    and addiction 15, 16, 20
    and alcohol 15, 19, 24, 25, 33
    and anxiety 2, 36
    and brain function 34–5
    and cannabis 15–16
    and crime 20
    and death 32, 33
    and depression 2
    and diabetes 35–6
    and drowning 33
    and drugs 15, 19–23, 24, 33
    and eating disorders 2
    and exercise 31–2, 33
    and gambling 16
    and gaming 16
    and health 13, 32
    and HIV 32–3
    and legal highs 16
    and meningitis 37–8
    and mental health 1–2, 4–7, 11, 12, 13, 14, 33, 36
    and mental illness 1, 5, 8
    and mobile phones 30
    and nutrition 33
    and obesity 34
    and phobias 2
    and rights 34
    and safety 36–7
    and self-harm 2, 10
    and septicaemia 37
    and sexual health 38–9
    and smoking 15, 16–19, 26–7, 34
    and social isolation 14
    and social networking 28–9
    and stress 10
    and suicide 2–3, 7–8, 9, 10
    and violence 33

Acknowledgements

The publisher is grateful for permission to reproduce the material in this book. While every care has been taken to trace and acknowledge copyright, the publisher tenders its apology for any accidental infringement or where copyright has proved untraceable. The publisher would be pleased to come to a suitable arrangement in any such case with the rightful owner.

Images

All images courtesy of iStock except page 3: Flaticon, page 6 © Alex Guillaume, page 28: Vectors and pages 20 and 37: Pixabay.

Icons

Icons on pages 13 and page 20 were made by Freepik from www.flaticon.com.

Illustrations

Don Hatcher: pages 12 & 35. Simon Kneebone: pages 23 & 39. Angelo Madrid: pages 14 & 30.

Additional acknowledgements

Editorial on behalf of Independence Educational Publishers by Cara Acred.

With thanks to the Independence team: Shelley Baldry, Tina Brand, Sandra Dennis, Jackie Staines and Jan Sunderland.

Cara Acred

Cambridge, September 2017